THE ULTIMATE
ARIZONA DIAMONDBACKS
TRIVIA BOOK

A Collection of Amazing Trivia Quizzes
and Fun Facts for Die-Hard D-backs Fans!

Ray Walker

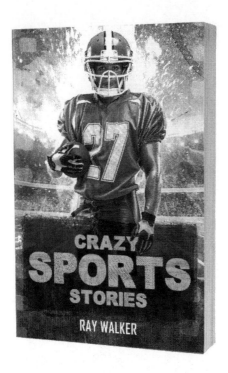

CONTENTS

INTRODUCTION

The Arizona Diamondbacks were established in 1998 as an expansion team. Even though they are one of the youngest teams in the league, they have consistently proven themselves to be a team who fights hard and is a force to be reckoned with in the MLB.

They currently hold one World Series championship, which they won in 2001. In addition, they have won one National League pennant, five NL West Division titles, and earned a Wild Card berth. They are quite often a threat in the National League West Division, and last winning it in 2011.

The Arizona Diamondbacks have retired the uniform numbers of Randy Johnson and Luis Gonzalez. They currently call Chase Field home, which opened in the same year they were established. The Dbacks play in one of the most difficult divisions in baseball, the National League West alongside the Los Angeles Dodgers Colorado Rockies, San Francisco Giants, and San Diego Padres.

The thing about baseball is that it is a lot like life, there are good times and bad times, good days and bad days, but you have to do your absolute best to never give up. The Arizona

1

Diamondbacks have proven that they refuse to give up and that they will do anything they need to do to bring a championship to the Valley of the Sun. While their history may not go back far, it is captivating non-the-less with many undeniable players to be profoundly proud of.

Being such a recent team, you're probably already very knowledgeable as the die-hard Dbacks fan that you are. Let's test that knowledge to see if you truly are the world's biggest Arizona Diamondbacks fan. All stats in this book are current as of the end of the 2020 season.

CHAPTER 1:

ORIGINS & HISTORY

QUIZ TIME!

1. Which of the following team names did the Arizona Diamondbacks franchise once go by?

    a. Arizona Phoenicians

    b. Arizona Suns

    c. Arizona Heat

    d. They have always been the Diamondbacks

2. In what year was the Arizona Diamondbacks franchise established?

    a. 1868

    b. 1978

    c. 1988

    d. 1998

3. The Arizona Diamondbacks' current home stadium is Chase Field.

    a. True

    b. False

4. Which division do the Arizona Diamondbacks play in currently?

    a. American League West
    b. National League West
    c. American League Central
    d. National League Central

5. The Arizona Diamondbacks have never won a Wild Card berth.

    a. True
    b. False

6. How many National League pennants have the Arizona Diamondbacks franchise won?

    a. 0
    b. 1
    c. 2
    d. 3

7. Who is the current principal owner of the Arizona Diamondbacks?

    a. Larry Dolan
    b. Robert Nutting
    c. Arturo Moreno
    d. Ken Kendrick

8. Who is the winningest manager in Arizona Diamondbacks history?

    a. Buck Showalter
    b. Bob Melvin

c. Kirk Gibson

d. Torey Lovullo

9. What is the name of the Arizona Diamondbacks' Triple-A team?

    a. Albuquerque Isotopes

    b. Jacksonville Jumbo Shrimp

    c. Toledo Mud Hens

    d. Reno Aces

10. Who was the first manager of the Arizona Diamondbacks' franchise?

    a. Buck Showalter

    b. Bob Brenly

    c. Al Pedrique

    d. Bob Melvin

11. The Arizona Diamondbacks were members of the American League West from 1998-2001.

    a. True

    b. False

12. What is the name of the Arizona Diamondbacks' current Spring Training home stadium?

    a. Goodyear Ballpark

    b. Hohokam Stadium

    c. Salt River Fields

    d. Sloan Park

13. How many appearances has the Arizona Diamondbacks franchise made in the MLB playoffs?

    a. 2
    b. 4
    c. 6
    d. 8

14. How many World Series titles have the Arizona Diamondbacks won?

    a. 0
    b. 1
    c. 2
    d. 3

15. The Arizona Diamondbacks current manager is Torey Lovullo.

    a. True
    b. False

16. Which stadium was the first home stadium of the Arizona Diamondbacks franchise?

    a. Camelback Field
    b. Sloan Park
    c. Phoenix Park
    d. Chase Field

17. Who is the current General Manager of the Arizona Diamondbacks?

    a. Mike Rizzo
    b. Mike Hazen

c. David Forst

d. Jerry Dipoto

18. How many National League West Division titles have the Arizona Diamondbacks won total?

   a. 3

   b. 5

   c. 7

   d. 10

19. Derrick Hall is the current President of Baseball Operations for the Arizona Diamondbacks.

   a. True

   b. False

20. Al Pedrique and A.J. Hinch are the only two Arizona Diamondbacks managers to not lead a team into the MLB playoffs in franchise history.

   a. True

   b. False

QUIZ ANSWERS

1. D – They have always been the Diamondbacks

2. D – 1998

3. A – True

4. B – National League West

5. B – False (2017)

6. B – 1

7. D – Ken Kendrick

8. C – Kirk Gibson

9. D – Reno Aces

10. A – Buck Showalter

11. B – False (they have always been in the NL West)

12. C – Salt River Fields

13. C – 6

14. B – 1

15. A – True

16. D – Chase Field (as Bank One Ballpark)

17. B – Mike Hazen

18. B – 5

19. A - True

20. B – False, Chip Hale did not either

DID YOU KNOW?

1. The Arizona Diamondbacks franchise has had nine managers so far in their history. They include Buck Showalter, Bob Brenly, Al Pedrique, Bob Melvin, A.J. Hinch, Kirk Gibson, Alan Trammell, Chip Hale, and Torey Lovullo.

2. The Arizona Diamondbacks' current manager is Torey Lovullo, who has been manager since 2017. He played in the MLB as an infielder for the Detroit Tigers, New York Yankees, California Angels, Seattle Mariners, Oakland A's, Cleveland Indians, and Philadelphia Phillies. He has also had a stint as manager of the Boston Red Sox in 2015. In addition, he had roles at the Toronto Blue Jays first base coach and as the Boston Red Sox's bench coach. Lovullo attended the University of California, Los Angeles (UCLA).

3. Kirk Gibson is the Arizona Diamondbacks' all-time winningest manager with a record of 353-375 for a .485 winning percentage. Kirk Gibson managed the Arizona Diamondbacks from 2010-2014. Gibson is a former MLB outfielder. He is a two-time World Series champion and spent his MLB career with the Detroit Tigers, Los Angeles Dodgers, Kansas City Royals and Pittsburgh Pirates.

4. The Arizona Diamondbacks became the fastest expansion team in MLB history to win a World Series championship.

5. The Arizona Diamondbacks franchise has hosted one All-Star Game so far in their history; 2011 at Chase Field.

6. The Arizona Diamondbacks have had two no-hitters thrown in franchise history, including one perfect game. Randy Johnson threw a perfect game on May 18, 2004, against the Atlanta Braves. Edwin Jackson threw a no-hitter on June 25, 2010, against the Tampa Bay Rays.

7. The Arizona Diamondbacks first MLB game was played on March 31, 1998, against the Colorado Rockies at Bank One Ballpark (Chase Field).

8. The Arizona Diamondbacks' Double-A team is the Amarillo Sod Poodles. High Single-A is the Hillsboro Hops. Low Single-A is the Visalia Rawhide.

9. The Arizona Diamondbacks' current mascot is a bobcat named "D. Baxter the Bobcat." He was inspired by the initials of the original name of Chase Field, Bank One Ballpark, or "BOB." Bobcats are wild cats, native to the state of Arizona. Baxter has been the Dbacks' mascot since 2000.

10. The Arizona Diamondbacks have retired two numbers so far in franchise history, three including Jackie Robinson's No. 42, which is retired league wide. Numbers retired include Randy Johnson's No. 51 and Luis Gonzalez's No. 20.

CHAPTER 2:

JERSEYS & NUMBERS

QUIZ TIME!

1. The Arizona Diamondbacks' original team colors were purple, black, teal and copper.

    a. True
    b. False

2. What are the Arizona Diamondbacks' current official team colors?

    a. Phoenix red, beige, black and white
    b. Phoenix red, beige, black, baby blue, and white
    c. Sedona red, Sonoran sand, black, teal, and white
    d. Sedona red, Sonoran sand, black, navy, and white

3. For the 2016 season, the Arizona Diamondbacks wore their throwback sleeveless pinstripe uniforms from their 2001 World Series Championship during Thursday home games.

    a. True
    b. False

4. Which of the following numbers is NOT retired by the Arizona Diamondbacks?

    a. 20

    b. 33

    c. 42

    d. 51

5. What uniform number does David Peralta currently wear as a member of the Arizona Diamondbacks?

    a. 6

    b. 16

    c. 26

    d. 36

6. What uniform number did Paul Goldschmidt wear during his time with the Arizona Diamondbacks?

    a. 14

    b. 24

    c. 34

    d. 44

7. Brandon Webb wore the uniform numbers 55 and 17 during his time with the Arizona Diamondbacks.

    a. True

    b. False

8. What uniform number did Curt Schilling wear during his time with the Arizona Diamondbacks?

    a. 18

    b. 28

c. 38

d. 48

9. Who is the only Arizona Diamondbacks player to have ever worn the uniform No. 99?

   a. Neil Weber

   b. Charles Brewer

   c. Brandon Drury

   d. Taijuan Walker

10. No Arizona Diamondbacks player has ever won the uniform No. 0.

   a. True

   b. False

11. What uniform number did A.J. Pollock wear as a member of the Arizona Diamondbacks?

   a. 1

   b. 11

   c. 21

   d. 31

12. What uniform number did Steve Finley wear as a member of the Arizona Diamondbacks?

   a. 2

   b. 12

   c. 22

   d. 32

13. Dan Haren wore the uniform number 15 during his time with the Arizona Diamondbacks.

a. True

b. False

14. What uniform number did Zack Greinke wear as a member of the Arizona Diamondbacks?

    a. 12

    b. 20

    c. 21

    d. Both B & C

15. What uniform number did Chris Young wear as a member of the Arizona Diamondbacks?

    a. 4

    b. 14

    c. 24

    d. None of the Above

16. What uniform number does Ketel Marte currently wear as a member of the Arizona Diamondbacks?

    a. 4

    b. 14

    c. 24

    d. 34

17. During his time with the Arizona Diamondbacks, Justin Upton wore which uniform number?

    a. 5

    b. 10

    c. 15

    d. 20

18. What uniform number did Mark Trumbo wear with the Arizona Diamondbacks?

    a. 5
    b. 10
    c. 15
    d. 20

19. What uniform number did Wade Miley wear as a member of the Arizona Diamondbacks?

    a. 16
    b. 36
    c. 46
    d. 56

20. J.J. Putz wore the uniform number 40 during his time with the Arizona Diamondbacks.

    a. True
    b. False

QUIZ ANSWERS

1. A - True

2. C – Sedona red, Sonoran sand, black, teal and white

3. A – True

4. B – 33

5. A – 6

6. D – 44

7. A – True

8. C – 38

9. D – Taijuan Walker

10. A – True

11. B – 11

12. B – 12

13. A – True

14. C – 21

15. C – 24

16. A – 4

17. B – 10

18. C – 15

19. B – 36

20. A – True

DID YOU KNOW?

1. The Arizona Diamondbacks have retired three uniform numbers overall so far in franchise history: Luis Gonzalez's No. 20, Randy Johnson's No. 51, and Jackie Robinson (No. 42).

2. During his time with the Arizona Diamondbacks, Jay Bell wore the uniform number 33.

3. During his time with the Arizona Diamondbacks, Willie Bloomquist wore the uniform number 18.

4. During his time with the Arizona Diamondbacks, Gerardo Parra wore the uniform numbers 9, 18, and 8.

5. During his time with the Arizona Diamondbacks, Aaron Hill wore the uniform number 2.

6. During his time with the Arizona Diamondbacks, Brad Ziegler wore the uniform number 29.

7. Jackie Robinson's No. 42 is retired by the Arizona Diamondbacks, as well as the MLB league wide, meaning no Diamondbacks or MLB player will ever wear No. 42 again. The Yankees' Mariano Rivera was the final player to wear it.

8. During his time with the Arizona Diamondbacks, Miguel Montero wore the uniform number 26.

9. During his time with the Arizona Diamondbacks, Eric Byrnes wore the uniform number 22.

10. During his time with the Arizona Diamondbacks, Stephen Drew wore the uniform number 6.

CHAPTER 3:

BIG UNIT

QUIZ TIME!

1. What is Randy Johnson's full name?

    a. Joseph Randall Johnson
    b. Randall Joseph Johnson
    c. Randall David Johnson
    d. David Randall Johnson

2. Randy Johnson played his entire 22-season MLB career with the Arizona Diamondbacks.

    a. True
    b. False

3. Where was Randy Johnson born?

    a. Sacramento, California
    b. Walnut Creek, California
    c. Phoenix, Arizona
    d. Tucson, Arizona

4. When was Randy Johnson born?

a. March 10, 1960

b. March 10, 1963

c. September 10, 1960

d. September 10, 1963

5. Randy Johnson won a pitching Triple Crown in 2002.

a. True

b. False

6. How many Cy Young Awards did Randy Johnson win over the course of his 22-season MLB career?

a. 2

b. 3

c. 5

d. 7

7. What year was Randy Johnson inducted into the National Baseball Hall of Fame with 97.3% of the vote?

a. 2013

b. 2014

c. 2015

d. 2016

8. Randy Johnson was named the 2001 World Series MVP.

a. True

b. False

9. How many World Series championships did Randy Johnson win over the course of his 22-season MLB career?

a. 0

b. 1

c. 2

d. 3

10. What year did Randy Johnson make his MLB debut?

    a. 1985

    b. 1986

    c. 1987

    d. 1988

11. How many All-Star Games was Randy Johnson named to over the course of his 22-season MLB career?

    a. 6

    b. 8

    c. 10

    d. 12

12. Randy Johnson's uniform No. 51 is retired by the Arizona Diamondbacks.

    a. True

    b. False

13. How many seasons of his MLB career did Randy Johnson spend with the Arizona Diamondbacks?

    a. 4

    b. 8

    c. 10

    d. 12

14. Randy Johnson recorded 4,875 strikeouts over the course of his 22-season MLB career.

a. True

b. False

15. How many times did Randy Johnson lead the league in ERA over the course of his 22-season MLB career?

a. 1

b. 2

c. 3

d. 4

16. What is Randy Johnson's career ERA?

a. 3.09

b. 3.19

c. 3.29

d. 3.39

17. On May 18, 2004, Randy Johnson at age 40 became the oldest pitcher in MLB history to throw a perfect game.

a. True

b. False

18. How many wins did Randy Johnson record over the course of his 22-season MLB career?

a. 301

b. 302

c. 303

d. 304

19. How many losses did Randy Johnson record over the course of his 22-season MLB career?

a. 155

b. 166

c. 177

d. 188

20. Randy Johnson attended college at USC.

a. True

b. False

QUIZ ANSWERS

1. C – Randall David Johnson

2. B – False (Diamondbacks, Seattle Mariners, Montreal Expos, New York Yankees, San Francisco Giants and Houston Astros)

3. B – Walnut Creek, California

4. D – September 10, 1963

5. A – True

6. C – 5

7. C – 2015

8. A – True

9. B – 1 (2001)

10. D – 1988

11. C – 10

12. A – True

13. B – 8

14. A – True

15. D – 4

16. C – 3.29

17. A - True

18. C – 303

19. B – 166

20. A – True

DID YOU KNOW?

1. Randy Johnson is one of only two pitchers, the other being Greg Maddux, to win the Cy Young Award in four consecutive seasons (1999–2002). In 1999, he joined Pedro Martínez and Gaylord Perry in winning the Cy Young Award in both the American and National Leagues.

2. Randy Johnson is one of 18 pitchers in MLB history to record a win against all 30 MLB franchises.

3. In 1982, as a senior, Randy Johnson struck out 121 batters in 66 innings, and threw a perfect game in his last high school start.

4. Randy Johnson guest starred in The Simpsons episode "Bart Has Two Mommies," which aired on March 19, 2006.

5. For most of his MLB career, Randy Johnson held the title of tallest player in MLB history at 6 feet 10 inches tall.

6. During spring training on March 24, 2001, Randy Johnson hit a dove with a fastball. Seriously, go watch it on YouTube.

7. Randy Johnson is the first member of the National Baseball Hall of Fame to be depicted in an Arizona Diamondbacks uniform on his plaque.

8. On May 8, 2001, Randy Johnson struck out 20 batters in a single game, against the Cincinnati Reds.

9. While attending USC, Randy Johnson played baseball (alongside Mark McGwire) as well as basketball.

10. Since retiring from the MLB, Randy Johnson has pursued a second career as a photographer.

CHAPTER 4:

CATCHY NICKNAMES

QUIZ TIME!

1. What nickname does Luis Gonzalez go by?

    a. Legs

    b. LuGon

    c. Gonzo

    d. Big G

2. Paul Goldschmidt goes by the nickname "Goldy."

    a. True

    b. False

3. What nickname does Randy Johnson go by?

    a. Big Machine

    b. Big Rand

    c. Big Man

    d. Big Unit

4. What nickname does A.J. Pollock go by?

    a. Polly

    b. Pollo

c. Lock

d. Alps

5. What nickname does Ketel Marte go by?

   a. The Pike

   b. El Nino

   c. Ketel Black

   d. Both A & B

6. Which nickname does Welington Castillo go by?

   a. Barbacoa

   b. Porkchop

   c. Beef

   d. Chicken

7. Curt Schilling goes by the simple nickname "Schill."

   a. True

   b. False

8. What nickname does David Peralta go by?

   a. Freight Train

   b. Double Decker Bus

   c. Big Plane

   d. Both A & B

9. What nickname does Craig Counsell go by?

   a. Barbacoa

   b. Porkchop

   c. Beef

   d. Chicken

10. What nickname does Willie Bloomquist go by?

   a. Knife

   b. Spork

   c. Fork

   d. Spoon

11. What nickname does Miguel Montero go by?

   a. Miggy

   b. Tero

   c. Monty

   d. Jelly

12. Zack Greinke's full name is Donald Zachary Greinke.

   a. True

   b. False

13. "J.J." is a nickname. What is J.J. Putz's full name?

   a. Joshua Jacob Putz

   b. Jacob Joshua Putz

   c. Joseph Jason Putz

   d. Jason Joseph Putz

14. What nickname does Madison Bumgarner go by?

   a. The Gardener

   b. Maddie

   c. Bummy

   d. MadBum

15. Wade Miley goes by the nickname "Miles."

   a. True

   b. False

16. What nickname does Gregg Olson go by?

    a. Snow Leopard
    b. Otter
    c. Kookaburra
    d. Zebra

17. Aaron Hill goes by the nickname "Hilly."

    a. True
    b. False

18. What nickname does Stephen Drew go by?

    a. Bark
    b. Mud
    c. Dirt
    d. Wood

19. What nickname does Patrick Corbin go by?

    a. Patty
    b. Blue
    c. Corby
    d. PAC

20. Justin Upton goes by the nickname "J-Up."

    a. True
    b. False

QUIZ ANSWERS

1. C – Gonzo

2. A – True

3. D – Big Unit

4. B – Pollo

5. D – Both A & B

6. C – Beef

7. A – True

8. A – Freight Train

9. D – Chicken

10. B – Spork

11. C – Monty

12. A – True

13. C – Joseph Jason Putz

14. D – MadBum

15. A - True

16. B – Otter

17. A – True

18. C – Dirt

19. C – Corby

20. A – True

DID YOU KNOW?

1. Jarrod Saltalamacchia goes by the nickname "Salty."

2. Former Dbacks manager Bob Melvin goes by the nickname "BoMel."

3. Former Dbacks manager Kirk Gibson goes by the nickname "Gibby."

4. Trevor Bauer goes by the nickname "Bauer Outage."

5. Eric Byrnes goes by the nickname "Byrnesie."

6. Mark Reynolds goes by the nicknames "Mega-Mark," "Sheriff of Swattingham," "Skeletor" and "Forrest Gump."

7. Matt Williams goes by the nicknames "Carson Crusher," "Matt the Bat" and "Big Marine."

8. Mark Grace goes by the nicknames "Amazing" and "Gracie."

9. "Didi" is a nickname. Didi Gregorius' full name is Mariekson Julius Gregorius.

10. Brad Ziegler goes by the nickname "Unicorn."

CHAPTER 5:

GONZO

QUIZ TIME!

1. What is Luis Gonzalez's full name?

   a. Eugene Luis Gonzalez

   b. Luis Eugene Gonzalez

   c. Luis Emilio Gonzalez

   d. Emilio Luis Gonzalez

2. Luis Gonzalez played his entire 19-season MLB career with the Arizona Diamondbacks.

   a. True

   b. False

3. Where was Luis Gonzalez born?

   a. Tampa, Florida

   b. Miami, Florida

   c. San Diego, California

   d. San Francisco, California

4. When was Luis Gonzalez born?

a. June 3, 1963

b. June 3, 1967

c. September 3, 1963

d. September 3, 1967

5. Luis Gonzalez did NOT win a World Series Championship over the course of his 19-season MLB career.

   a. True

   b. False

6. How many total All-Star Games was Luis Gonzalez named to over the course of his 19-season MLB career?

   a. 2

   b. 4

   c. 5

   d. 8

7. What year did Luis Gonzalez win the Home Run Derby?

   a. 2000

   b. 2001

   c. 2002

   d. 2003

8. Luis Gonzalez was inducted into the National Baseball Hall of Fame in 2014.

   a. True

   b. False

9. How many Silver Slugger Awards did Luis Gonzalez win over the course of his 19-season MLB career?

a. 1

b. 2

c. 3

d. 4

10. Luis Gonzalez was childhood friends with which former MLB star?

    a. Ivan Rodriguez

    b. Albert Pujols

    c. Tino Martinez

    d. Alex Rodriguez

11. How many total home runs did Luis Gonzalez hit over the course of his 19-season MLB career?

    a. 324

    b. 334

    c. 344

    d. 354

12. Luis Gonzalez was the first player to have his uniform number retired by the Arizona Diamondbacks.

    a. True

    b. False

13. What is Luis Gonzalez's career batting average?

    a. .263

    b. .273

    c. .283

    d. .293

14. Luis Gonzalez won a Branch Rickey Award in 2005.

    a. True
    b. False

15. How many hits did Luis Gonzalez collect over the course of his 19-season MLB career?

    a. 2,581
    b. 2,591
    c. 2,601
    d. 2,611

16. How many RBIs did Luis Gonzalez collect over the course of his 19-season MLB career?

    a. 1,239
    b. 1,339
    c. 1,439
    d. 1,539

17. Over the course of his 19-season MLB career, Luis Gonzalez was named the National League Player of the Month twice.

    a. True
    b. False

18. Over the course of his 19-season MLB career, how many times was Luis Gonzalez named the National League Player of the Week?

    a. 1
    b. 2

c. 3

d. 4

19. Where did Luis Gonzalez attend college?

    a. University of California at Los Angeles

    b. University of Florida

    c. University of South Alabama

    d. He did not attend college

20. Luis Gonzalez's career WAR is 51.6.

    a. True

    b. False

QUIZ ANSWERS

1. C – Luis Emilio Gonzalez

2. B – False (Diamondbacks, Houston Astros, Chicago Cubs, Los Angeles Dodgers, Florida Marlins and Detroit Tigers)

3. A – Tampa, Florida

4. D – September 3, 1967

5. B – False (1 in 2001)

6. C – 5

7. B – 2001

8. B – False (Only got 0.9% of the vote)

9. A – 1

10. C – Tino Martinez

11. D – 354

12. A – True

13. C - .283

14. A – True

15. B – 2,591

16. C – 1, 439

17. A – True (April 2001, June 2001)

18. D – 4 (June 11, 2000, July 30, 2000, June 24, 2001 & June 6, 2004)

19. C – University of South Alabama

20. A – True

DID YOU KNOW?

1. Over the course of his 19-season MLB career, Luis Gonzalez had 9,157 at-bats.

2. Over the course of his 19-season MLB career, Luis Gonzalez stole 128 bases.

3. Over the course of his 19-season MLB career, Luis Gonzalez spent eight seasons with the Arizona Diamondbacks, seven seasons with the Houston Astros, two seasons with the Chicago Cubs, one season with the Los Angeles Dodgers, one with the Florida Marlins and one season with the Detroit Tigers.

4. In 2009, Luis Gonzalez became the Special Assistant to the President for the Arizona Diamondbacks.

5. Luis Gonzalez hit the series-winning hit in Game 7 of the 2001 World Series off Mariano Rivera of the New York Yankees.

6. Luis Gonzalez's son, Jacob, was drafted by the San Francisco Giants in 2017.

7. Luis Gonzalez was inducted into the Hispanic Heritage Baseball Museum Hall of Fame in 2011.

8. Luis Gonzalez lent his name to a restaurant called "Gonzo's" in Gilbert, Arizona. It closed in 2004.

9. The Arizona Diamondbacks built a Little League field in Luis Gonzalez's honor at Tempe Beach Park.

10. Luis Gonzalez made his MLB debut on September 4, 1990, and played in his final MLB game on September 28, 2008.

CHAPTER 6:

STATISTICALLY SPEAKING

QUIZ TIME!

1. Luis Gonzalez currently holds the Arizona Diamondbacks franchise record for the most home runs. How many home runs did he hit over the course of his career in Arizona?

    a. 214
    b. 224
    c. 234
    d. 244

2. Pitcher Randy Johnson has the most wins in Arizona Diamondbacks franchise history with 118.

    a. True
    b. False

3. Which pitcher holds the Arizona Diamondbacks record for most career shutouts thrown with 14?

    a. Dan Haren
    b. Brandon Webb

c. Curt Schilling

d. Randy Johnson

4. Which Arizona Diamondbacks batter currently holds the single season record for strikeouts with 223?

   a. Justin Upton

   b. Adam LaRoche

   c. Mark Reynolds

   d. Paul Goldschmidt

5. Pitcher Randy Johnson has the most strikeouts in Arizona Diamondbacks franchise history with how many?

   a. 1,777

   b. 1,877

   c. 1,977

   d. 2,077

6. Tony Womack has the most stolen bases in Arizona Diamondbacks franchise history with how many?

   a. 162

   b. 172

   c. 182

   d. 192

7. Jose Valverde holds the record for most saves in Arizona Diamondbacks history with 98.

   a. True

   b. False

8. Who holds the Arizona Diamondbacks record for being intentionally walked with 103?

a. Luis Gonzalez

b. Paul Goldschmidt

c. Miguel Montero

d. Gerardo Parra

9. Which player holds the Arizona Diamondbacks franchise record for home runs in a single season with 57?

a. Luis Gonzalez

b. Mark Reynolds

c. Jay Bell

d. Troy Glaus

10. Which batter holds the single season Arizona Diamondbacks record for hits with 206?

a. Aaron Hill

b. Jean Segura

c. Luis Gonzalez

d. Paul Goldschmidt

11. Which player holds the single season Arizona Diamondbacks record for double plays grounded into with 29?

a. Justin Upton

b. Paul Goldschmidt

c. Orlando Hudson

d. Martin Prado

12. Luis Gonzalez holds the record for the most sacrifice flies in Arizona Diamondbacks all-time franchise history with 44.

a. True

b. False

13. Brandon Webb threw the most wild pitches in Arizona Diamondbacks franchise history with how many?

 a. 46

 b. 56

 c. 66

 d. 76

14. Tony Womack holds the Arizona Diamondbacks single season record for most triples. How many did he hit in 2000?

 a. 12

 b. 14

 c. 18

 d. 21

15. Which hitter has the most walks in Arizona Diamondbacks franchise history with 655?

 a. Justin Upton

 b. Chris Young

 c. Paul Goldschmidt

 d. Luis Gonzalez

16. Which Arizona Diamondbacks hitter holds the all-time franchise record for best overall batting average at .298?

 a. Orlando Hudson

 b. Danny Bautista

 c. Paul Goldschmidt

 d. Luis Gonzalez

17. Luis Gonzalez holds the Arizona Diamondbacks record for most runs scored with 780.

    a. True
    b. False

18. Luis Gonzalez has the most plate appearances all time in Arizona Diamondbacks franchise history with how many?

    a. 5,046
    b. 5,146
    c. 5,246
    d. 5,346

19. Which pitcher holds the Arizona Diamondbacks franchise record for most saves in a single season with 47?

    a. J.J. Putz
    b. Jose Valverde
    c. Fernando Rodney
    d. Brad Ziegler

20. Randy Johnson and Brandon Webb are tied for the Arizona Diamondbacks franchise record for most losses with 62 each.

    a. True
    b. False

QUIZ ANSWERS

1. B – 224

2. A - True

3. D – Randy Johnson

4. C – Mark Reynolds (2009)

5. D – 2,077

6. C – 182

7. A – True

8. B – Paul Goldschmidt

9. A – Luis Gonzalez (2001)

10. C – Luis Gonzalez (1999) -

11. D – Martin Prado (2013)

12. A – True

13. B – 56

14. B – 14

15. C – Paul Goldschmidt

16. D – Luis Gonzalez

17. A – True

18. C – 5,246

19. B – Jose Valverde (2007)

20. A – True

DID YOU KNOW?

1. Randy Johnson threw the most innings in Arizona Diamondbacks franchise history with 1,630.1. Coming in second is Brandon Webb who threw 1,319.2 innings.

2. Luis Gonzalez had the best single season batting average in Arizona Diamondbacks franchise history at .336 in 1999. Coming in second is Ketel Marte whose batting average was .329 in 2019.

3. Chris Owings holds the Arizona Diamondbacks franchise record for stolen base percentage with 84.34% accuracy. Tony Womack holds the Arizona Diamondbacks franchise record for stolen bases with 182. Tony Womack also holds the Arizona Diamondbacks franchise record for the most times caught stealing at 46 times.

4. Luis Gonzalez has the most extra-base hits in Arizona Diamondbacks franchise history with 561. Second on the list is Paul Goldschmidt with 495.

5. Mark Reynolds holds the Arizona Diamondbacks franchise record for at-bats per home run at 16.4. Essentially what this means is that on average, Reynolds hit a home run about every 16-17 at-bats.

6. Randy Johnson holds the Arizona Diamondbacks franchise record for strikeouts per nine innings pitched at 11.466. Essentially what this means is that during his time

with the Dbacks, Johnson recorded about 11-12 strikeouts in every nine innings that he pitched.

7. Luis Gonzalez holds the Arizona Diamondbacks record for the most hit by pitches with 61. Randy Johnson holds the Arizona Diamondbacks record for most batters hit with 74.

8. Luis Gonzalez holds the Arizona Diamondbacks franchise record for career doubles hit with 310. Second on the list is Paul Goldschmidt with 267.

9. Randy Johnson holds the Arizona Diamondbacks single season record for wins with 24 in 2002. Rodrigo Lopez and Brandon Webb are tied for the Arizona Diamondbacks single season record for most losses with 16 each. Lopez had 16 losses in 2010 and Webb had 16 losses in 2004.

10. Mark Reynolds holds the Arizona Diamondbacks franchise record for most strikeouts in a single season with 223 in 2009.

CHAPTER 7:

THE TRADE MARKET

QUIZ TIME!

1. On July 31, 2019, the Arizona Diamondbacks traded Zack Greinke and cash considerations to which team in exchange for Corbin Martin, Josh Rojas, J.B. Bukauskas and Seth Beer?

    a. Milwaukee Brewers

    b. Kansas City Royals

    c. Houston Astros

    d. Los Angeles Dodgers

2. On December 5, 2018, the Arizona Diamondbacks traded Paul Goldschmidt to which team in exchange for Carson Kelly, Luke Weaver, Andrew Young and a 2019 competitive balance round B pick?

    a. Oakland Athletics

    b. Washington Nationals

    c. Los Angeles Dodgers

    d. St. Louis Cardinals

3. The Arizona Diamondbacks have made 12 total trades with the Oakland Athletics.

   a. True
   b. False

4. On July 18, 2017, the Arizona Diamondbacks traded Sergio Alcantara, Dawel Lugo and Jose King to which team in exchange for J.D. Martinez?

   a. Boston Red Sox
   b. Houston Astros
   c. Detroit Tigers
   d. Minnesota Twins

5. The Arizona Diamondbacks have made 11 trades with the Tampa Bay Rays all time.

   a. True
   b. False

6. On November 23, 2016, the Arizona Diamondbacks traded Mitch Haniger, Jean Segura, and Zac Curtis to which team in exchange for Ketel Marte and Taijuan Walker?

   a. New York Mets
   b. Seattle Mariners
   c. Toronto Blue Jays
   d. Philadelphia Phillies

7. On December 9, 2015, the Arizona Diamondbacks traded Aaron Blair, Ender Inciarte, and Dansby Swanson to which team in exchange for Shelby Miller and Gabe Speier?

a. Chicago Cubs

b. Texas Rangers

c. St. Louis Cardinals

d. Atlanta Braves

8. On January 24, 2013, the Arizona Diamondbacks traded Justin Upton and Chris Johnson to which team in exchange for Nick Ahmed, Randall Delgado, Brandon Drury, Martin Prado, and Zeke Spruill?

a. Los Angeles Angels

b. Atlanta Braves

c. San Diego Padres

d. Detroit Tigers

9. As a part of a three-team trade on December 11, 2012, the Arizona Diamondbacks traded Trevor Bauer, Matt Albers, and Bryan Shaw to which team?

a. Cincinnati Reds

b. Los Angeles Dodgers

c. Cleveland Indians

d. Colorado Rockies

10. The Arizona Diamondbacks have made only four trades with the San Diego Padres all time.

a. True

b. False

11. As part of a three-team trade on December 8, 2009, the Arizona Diamondbacks traded which player along with Daniel Schlereth to the Detroit Tigers?

a. Max Scherzer

b. Dan Haren

c. Brandon Webb

d. Yusmeiro Petit

12. The Arizona Diamondbacks have made seven trades with the Colorado Rockies all time.

a. True

b. False

13. On December 1, 2003, the Arizona Diamondbacks traded Chris Capuano, Craig Counsell, Lyle Overbay, Jorge De La Rosa, and Chad Moeller to which team in exchange for Richie Sexon, Shance Nance, and a player to be named later (Noochie Varner)?

a. New York Yankees

b. Seattle Mariners

c. Cleveland Indians

d. Milwaukee Brewers

14. The Arizona Diamondbacks have made 11 trades with the Florida/Miami Marlins all time.

a. True

b. False

15. On July 26, 2000, the Arizona Diamondbacks traded Omar Daal, Nelson Figueroa, Travis Lee, and Vicente Padilla to which team in exchange for Curt Schilling?

a. Boston Red Sox

b. Philadelphia Phillies

c. Baltimore Orioles

d. Houston Astros

16. On July 8, 1999, the Arizona Diamondbacks traded Brad Penny, Vladimir Nuñez, and a player to be named later (Abraham Nunez) to which team in exchange for Matt Mantei?

   a. Los Angeles Dodgers
   b. Montreal Expos
   c. Florida Marlins
   d. Boston Red Sox

17. On February 25, 1999, the Arizona Diamondbacks traded a player to be named later (Jason Boyd) to which team in exchange for Tony Womack?

   a. Pittsburgh Pirates
   b. Chicago Cubs
   c. Cincinnati Reds
   d. Colorado Rockies

18. On December 28, 1998, the Arizona Diamondbacks traded Karim Garcia to which team in exchange for Luis Gonzalez?

   a. Los Angeles Dodgers
   b. Chicago Cubs
   c. Houston Astros
   d. Detroit Tigers

19. On December 1, 1997, the Arizona Diamondbacks traded Travis Fryman, Tom Martin, and cash considerations to which team in exchange for Matt Williams?

a. Colorado Rockies

b. Detroit Tigers

c. Cleveland Indians

d. San Francisco Giants

20. The Arizona Diamondbacks have made six trades with the San Francisco Giants all time.

a. True

b. False

QUIZ ANSWERS

1. C – Houston Astros

2. D – St. Louis Cardinals

3. A – True

4. C – Detroit Tigers

5. A – True

6. B – Seattle Mariners

7. D – Atlanta Braves

8. B – Atlanta Braves

9. C – Cleveland Indians

10. A – True

11. A – Max Scherzer

12. A – True

13. D – Milwaukee Brewers

14. A – True

15. B – Philadelphia Phillies

16. C – Florida Marlins

17. A – Pittsburgh Pirates

18. D – Houston Astros

19. C – Cleveland Indians

20. A – True

DID YOU KNOW?

1. On January 11, 2005, the Arizona Diamondbacks traded Randy Johnson to the New York Yankees. The Yankees traded him back to the Dbacks on January 9, 2007.

2. On July 25, 2010, the Arizona Diamondbacks traded Dan Haren to the Los Angeles Angels of Anaheim in exchange for Patrick Corbin, Joe Saunders, Rafael Rodriguez, and a player to be named later (Tyler Skaggs).

3. On July 31, 2011, the Arizona Diamondbacks traded Jordan Norberto and Brandon Allen to the Oakland A's in exchange for Brad Ziegler.

4. On August 5, 2004, the Arizona Diamondbacks traded Roberto Alomar to the Chicago White Sox in exchange for a player to be named later (Brad Murray).

5. On August 23, 2011, the Arizona Diamondbacks traded Kelly Johnson to the Toronto Blue Jays in exchange for Aaron Hill and John McDonald.

6. The Arizona Diamondbacks have made only five trades all time with the Baltimore Orioles.

7. The Arizona Diamondbacks have made 15 trades all time with the New York Yankees.

8. The Arizona Diamondbacks have made only eight trades all time with the Los Angeles Dodgers.

9. The Arizona Diamondbacks have made only six trades all time with the Minnesota Twins.

10. The Arizona Diamondbacks have made only three trades all time with the Texas Rangers.

CHAPTER 8:

DRAFT DAY

QUIZ TIME!

1. Randy Johnson was drafted by which in the second round of the 1985 MLB Draft?

    a. New York Yankees
    b. Seattle Mariners
    c. Montreal Expos
    d. Houston Astros

2. Paul Goldschmidt was drafted by the Arizona Diamondbacks in which round of the 2009 MLB Draft?

    a. 2nd
    b. 4th
    c. 6th
    d. 8th

3. Brandon Webb was drafted by the Arizona Diamondbacks in which round of the 2000 MLB Draft?

    a. 6th
    b. 7th

c. 8th

d. 9th

4. Luis Gonzalez was drafted by which team in the fourth round of the 1988 MLB Draft?

    a. Chicago Cubs

    b. Houston Astros

    c. Los Angeles Dodgers

    d. Detroit Tigers

5. Curt Schilling was drafted by which team in the second round of the 1986 MLB Draft?

    a. Boston Red Sox

    b. Philadelphia Phillies

    c. Baltimore Orioles

    d. Houston Astros

6. With which pick in the first round of the 2009 MLB Draft did the Arizona Diamondbacks select A.J. Pollock?

    a. 13th

    b. 15th

    c. 17th

    d. 19th

7. Steve Finley was drafted by the Baltimore Orioles in the 13th round of the 1987 MLB Draft.

    a. True

    b. False

8. With the sixth overall pick in the first round of the 2002 MLB Draft, which team selected Zack Greinke?

a. Arizona Diamondbacks

b. Kansas City Royals

c. Los Angeles Dodgers

d. Milwaukee Brewers

9. Dan Haren was drafted by which team in the second round of the 2001 MLB Draft?

a. Los Angeles Dodgers

b. Los Angeles Angels

c. Oakland A's

d. St. Louis Cardinals

10. Chris Young was drafted by the Chicago White Sox in the 16th round of the 2001 MLB Draft.

a. True

b. False

11. With which overall pick in the first round of the 2005 MLB Draft did the Arizona Diamondbacks select Justin Upton?

a. 1st

b. 2nd

c. 9th

d. 10th

12. Matt Williams was drafted by the San Francisco Giants in the first round (third overall) of the 1986 MLB Draft.

a. True

b. False

13. Craig Counsell was drafted by which team in the 11th round of the 1992 MLB Draft?

    a. Los Angeles Dodgers
    b. Florida Marlins
    c. Colorado Rockies
    d. Milwaukee Brewers

14. With which overall pick in the first round of the 2008 MLB Draft did the Arizona Diamondbacks select Wade Miley?

    a. 10th
    b. 21st
    c. 32nd
    d. 43rd

15. J.J. Putz was drafted by which team in the sixth round of the 1999 MLB Draft?

    a. Chicago White Sox
    b. Seattle Mariners
    c. New York Mets
    d. Arizona Diamondbacks

16. With which overall pick in the first round of the 2011 MLB Draft did the Arizona Diamondbacks select Trevor Bauer?

    a. 1st
    b. 2nd
    c. 3rd
    d. 4th

17. Brad Ziegler was drafted by which team in the 20th round of the 2003 MLB Draft?

    a. Miami Marlins
    b. Oakland A's
    c. Philadelphia Phillies
    d. Boston Red Sox

18. Willie Bloomquist was drafted by which team in the third round of the 1999 MLB Draft?

    a. Kansas City Royals
    b. Seattle Mariners
    c. Cincinnati Reds
    d. Arizona Diamondbacks

19. Patrick Corbin was drafted by which team in the second round of the 2009 MLB Draft?

    a. Washington Nationals
    b. Arizona Diamondbacks
    c. Los Angeles Angels of Anaheim
    d. New York Yankees

20. Madison Bumgarner was drafted by the San Francisco Giants in the first round (10th overall) of the 2007 MLB Draft.

    a. True
    b. False

QUIZ ANSWERS

1. C – Montreal Expos

2. D – 8th

3. C – 8th

4. B – Houston Astros

5. A – Boston Red Sox

6. C – 17th

7. A – True

8. B – Kansas City Royals

9. D – St. Louis Cardinals

10. A – True

11. A – 1st

12. A – True

13. C – Colorado Rockies

14. D – 43rd

15. B – Seattle Mariners

16. C – 3rd

17. C – Philadelphia Phillies

18. B – Seattle Mariners

19. C – Los Angeles Angels of Anaheim

20. A – True

DID YOU KNOW?

1. Eric Byrnes was drafted in the eighth round of the 1998 MLB Draft by the Oakland Athletics.

2. Stephen Vogt was drafted in the 12th round of the 2007 MLB Draft by the Tampa Bay Devil Rays.

3. Stephen Drew was drafted in the first round (15th overall) of the 2004 MLB Draft by the Arizona Diamondbacks.

4. Chris Young was drafted in the 16th round of the 2001 MLB Draft by the Chicago White Sox.

5. Aaron Hill was drafted in the first round (13th overall) of the 2003 MLB Draft by the Toronto Blue Jays.

6. Lyle Overbay was drafted in the 18th round of the 1999 MLB Draft by the Arizona Diamondbacks.

7. Tony Womack was drafted in the seventh round of the 1991 MLB Draft by the Pittsburgh Pirates.

8. Jay Bell was drafted in the first round (eighth overall) of the 1984 MLB Draft by the Minnesota Twins.

9. Former Dbacks manager Kirk Gibson was drafted in the first round (12th overall) of the 1978 MLB Draft by the Detroit Tigers.

10. Former Dbacks manager Bob Melvin was drafted in the first round (second overall) of the 1981 MLB Draft by the Detroit Tigers.

CHAPTER 9:

ODDS & ENDS

QUIZ TIME!

1. What is the name of Bronson Arroyo's 2005 debut album?

   a. *Rockin with Bronson*

   b. *Life's a Grand Slam*

   c. *Covering the Bases*

   d. *Another Day, Another Strikeout*

2. Madison Bumgarner once dated a girl named Madison Bumgarner.

   a. True

   b. False

3. Zack Greinke is a minority owner of a franchise of which fast food chain?

   a. In n Out

   b. Dunkin Donuts

   c. Chipotle

   d. Ben & Jerry's

4. In 2019, Eric Byrnes set the Guinness World Record for doing what?

   a. Fastest 100 Meter Hurdles Wearing Swim Fins
   b. Most Holes of Golf in a Single Day
   c. Most Pull Ups in 24 Hours
   d. Fastest 50 Meters Walking on Hands with a Soccer Ball Between the Legs

5. What MLB team was Paul Goldschmidt a fan of while growing up?

   a. Oakland A's
   b. Houston Astros
   c. St. Louis Cardinals
   d. New York Yankees

6. When Stephen Vogt was with the Oakland A's, he did an impersonation of which popular Saturday Night Live sketch character?

   a. Macgruber
   b. Matt Foley
   c. Stefon
   d. Church Lady

7. J.J. Putz shared a dorm building with NFL quarterback Tom Brady while at the University of Michigan.

   a. True
   b. False

8. Brandon Webb was inducted into the University of Kentucky Athletics Hall of Fame in 2009.

a. True

b. False

9. Who, along with Matt Herges, are the only two players in MLB history to play for all 5 National League West teams?

a. Craig Counsell

b. Edwin Jackson

c. Zach Greinke

d. Steve Finley

10. What NFL team's games did A.J. Pollock routinely attend while growing up?

a. Buffalo Bills

b. New York Jets

c. New England Patriots

d. Dallas Cowboys

11. Who has played for more MLB teams than any other player in MLB history?

a. Randy Johnson

b. Zack Greinke

c. Edwin Jackson

d. Justin Upton

12. Former Dback Justin Upton is the brother of fellow MLB star, B.J. Upton.

a. True

b. False

13. In 2007, Chris Young became the first rookie in MLB history to hit how many home runs and steal 25 bases?

a. 20

b. 25

c. 30

d. 35

14. Dan Haren beat all 30 MLB teams over the course of his MLB career.

a. True

b. False

15. In 2020, former Dback Jay Bell became manager of the Rocket City Trash Pandas, the Double-A affiliate of which team?

a. Chicago Cubs

b. Los Angeles Angels

c. Miami Marlins

d. Seattle Mariners

16. Stephen Drew is the brother of fellow MLB players J.D. Drew and Tim Drew.

a. True

b. False

17. Which former Arizona Diamondbacks player was recently named the head coach of Arizona State University baseball team?

a. Mark Grace

b. Lyle Overbay

c. Willie Bloomquist

d. Jay Bell

18. Brad Ziegler is a collector of what collectable?

    a. Superhero Figurines

    b. Coins

    c. Snowglobes

    d. Baseball Cards

19. Which MLB team was Wade Miley a fan of while growing up?

    a. Texas Rangers

    b. Atlanta Braves

    c. Houston Astros

    d. Tampa Bay Devil Rays

20. In 2015, former Arizona Diamondbacks manager Kirk Gibson was diagnosed with Parkinson's Disease.

    a. True

    b. False

QUIZ ANSWERS

1. C – *Covering the Bases*

2. A – True

3. C – Chipotle

4. B – Most Holes of Golf in a Single Day (420 holes)

5. B – Houston Astros

6. B – Matt Foley (Van Down by the River Guy)

7. A – True

8. A – True

9. D – Steve Finley

10. C – New England Patriots

11. C – Edwin Jackson

12. A – True

13. C – 30

14. A – True

15. B – Los Angeles Angels

16. A – True

17. C – Willie Bloomquist

18. D – Baseball Cards

19. B – Atlanta Braves

20. A – True

DID YOU KNOW?

1. Curt Schilling is one of only 12 players born in the state of Alaska to play in the MLB.

2. Madison Bumgarner was raised in a place in North Carolina nicknamed Bumtown.

3. Former Diamondback Dan Plesac has a nephew, Zach, who currently pitches for the Cleveland Indians.

4. Former Arizona Diamondbacks players/coaches who are now analysts on MLB Network include Dan Plesac, Chris Young and Buck Showalter.

5. Josh Reddick is an avid wrestling fan. He even wrote an article about his love for wrestling in *The Player's Tribune.*

6. Aaron Hill was the first player since 1931 to hit for the cycle twice in a single season when he did so during the 2012 season.

7. Brandon McCarthy is a part owner of the Phoenix Rising FC. He is also currently the Special Assistant to the General Manager for the Texas Rangers.

8. While attending college at San Diego State University, Travis Lee received a Golden Spikes Award, given annually to the best college baseball player by USA Baseball.

9. In 2016, Gregg Olson helped coach actress Kylie Bunbury, who played "Ginny Baker" on the FOX show *Pitch.* The

show was a fictional adaptation of the MLB's first female player who played for the San Diego Padres.

10. Quinton McCracken's wife, Maggie, was a cast member on VH1's *Baseball Wives* reality show.

CHAPTER 10:

OUTFIELDERS

QUIZ TIME!

1. What is Luis Gonzalez's career batting average?

   a. .273

   b. .283

   c. .293

   d. .303

2. A.J. Pollock spent seven seasons of his MLB career with the Arizona Diamondbacks.

   a. True

   b. False

3. How many Gold Glove Awards did Steve Finley win over the course of his 19-season MLB career?

   a. 1

   b. 3

   c. 5

   d. 7

4. Chris Young was named to one All-Star Game over the course of his 13-season MLB career.

   a. True

   b. False

5. How many Silver Slugger Awards has Justin Upton won?

   a. 1

   b. 2

   c. 3

   d. 4

6. How many total seasons did Eric Byrnes spend with the Arizona Diamondbacks?

   a. 2

   b. 4

   c. 6

   d. 8

7. Gerardo Parra was named the 2009 National League Rookie of the Year.

   a. True

   b. False

8. How many Gold Glove Awards has Ender Inciarte won?

   a. 0

   b. 1

   c. 2

   d. 3

9. How many All-Star Games was Mark Trumbo named to over the course of his 10-season MLB career?

a. 1

b. 2

c. 3

d. 4

10. How many seasons did Tony Womack spend with the Diamondbacks?

a. 3

b. 4

c. 5

d. 6

11. Over the course of his 12-season MLB career, Danny Bautista played for the Arizona Diamondbacks, Detroit Tigers, Atlanta Braves, and which other franchise?

a. New York Mets

b. San Francisco Giants

c. Montreal Expos

d. Florida Marlins

12. Reggie Sanders was named to three All-Star Games over the course of his 17-season MLB career.

a. True

b. False

13. How many seasons did Quinton McCracken spend with the Arizona Diamondbacks?

a. 2

b. 4

c. 6

d. 8

14. How many Silver Slugger Awards did Shawn Green win over the course of his 15-season MLB career?

    a. 1
    b. 2
    c. 3
    d. 4

15. How many All-Star Games was Carlos Quentin named to over the course of his 9-season MLB career?

    a. 1
    b. 2
    c. 3
    d. 4

16. How many Gold Glove Awards has David Peralta won?

    a. 0
    b. 1
    c. 2
    d. 3

17. How many Gold Glove Awards did Michael Bourn win over the course of his 11-season MLB career?

    a. 0
    b. 1
    c. 2
    d. 3

18. How many seasons did Brandon Drury spend with the Arizona Diamondbacks?

a. 1

b. 2

c. 3

d. 4

19. How many All-Star Games has Ketel Marte been named to?

a. 1

b. 2

c. 3

d. 4

20. Kole Calhoun has played for the Arizona Diamondbacks and the Los Angeles Angels.

a. True

b. False

QUIZ ANSWERS

1. B – .283

2. A – True

3. C – 5

4. A – True

5. C – 3

6. B – 4

7. B – False (He came in 8th place)

8. D – 3

9. B – 2

10. C – 5

11. D – Florida Marlins

12. B – False (1)

13. B – 4

14. A – 1

15. B – 2

16. B – 1

17. C – 2

18. C – 3

19. A – 1

20. A – True

DID YOU KNOW?

1. Luis Gonzalez spent eight seasons of his 19-season MLB career with the Arizona Diamondbacks. He also played for the Houston Astros, Chicago Cubs, Los Angeles Dodgers, Florida Marlins, and Detroit Tigers. He is a five-time All-Star, 2001 Home Run Derby champion, 2001 World Series champion and 2001 Silver Slugger Award winner.

2. A.J. Pollock spent seven seasons of his MLB career with the Arizona Diamondbacks. He currently plays for the Los Angeles Dodgers. He was named an All-Star in 2015, the same year he won a Gold Glove Award winner, and he is also a 2020 World Series champion.

3. Steve Finley spent six seasons of his 19-season MLB career with the Arizona Diamondbacks. He also played for the San Diego Padres, Houston Astros, Baltimore Orioles, Colorado Rockies, San Francisco Giants, Los Angeles Dodgers, and Los Angeles Angels. He is a two-time All-Star, five-time Gold Glove Award winner, and 2001 World Series champion.

4. Justin Upton spent six seasons of his MLB career with the Arizona Diamondbacks and currently plays for the Los Angeles Angels. He has also played for the Atlanta Braves, Detroit Tigers, and San Diego Padres. He is a four-time All-Star and three-time Silver Slugger Award winner.

5. Chris Young spent seven seasons of his MLB career with the Arizona Diamondbacks. He also played for the Oakland A's, New York Yankees, Boston Red Sox, New York Mets, and Los Angeles Angels. He was an All-Star in 2010.

6. Gerardo Parra spent six seasons of his MLB career with the Arizona Diamondbacks and currently plays for the Washington Nationals. So far in his career, he has also played for the Colorado Rockies, Milwaukee Brewers, San Francisco Giants, and Baltimore Orioles. He is a two-time Gold Glove Award winner, 2019 World Series champion and the 2013 Wilson Overall Defensive Player of the Year Award winner.

7. Mark Trumbo spent two seasons of his 10-season MLB career with the Arizona Diamondbacks. He also played for the Los Angeles Angels, Baltimore Orioles, and Seattle Mariners. He is a two-time All-Star and a 2016 Silver Slugger Award winner.

8. Tony Womack spent five seasons of his 13-season MLB career with the Arizona Diamondbacks. He also played for the Pittsburgh Pirates, Chicago Cubs, Cincinnati Reds, Colorado Rockies, New York Yankees, and St. Louis Cardinals. He was an All-Star in 1997 and a 2001 World Series champion.

9. Kole Calhoun has been with the Arizona Diamondbacks since 2020 and has also played for the Los Angeles Angels where he won a Gold Glove Award in 2015.

10. Ketel Marte has been with the Arizona Diamondbacks since 2017. He has also played for the Seattle Mariners. He was an All-Star in 2019.

CHAPTER 11:

INFIELDERS

QUIZ TIME!

1. How many Silver Slugger Awards has Paul Goldschmidt won?

    a. 2

    b. 4

    c. 6

    d. 8

2. Jay Bell won a World Series with the Arizona Diamondbacks in 2001.

    a. True

    b. False

3. How many All-Star Games was Matt Williams named to over the course of his 17-season MLB career?

    a. 1

    b. 2

    c. 5

    d. 6

4. How many Gold Glove Awards did Mark Grace win over the course of his 16-season MLB career?

    a. 1
    b. 2
    c. 3
    d. 4

5. How many seasons did Craig Counsell spend with the Arizona Diamondbacks?

    a. 2
    b. 4
    c. 6
    d. 8

6. How many seasons did Lyle Overbay spend with the Arizona Diamondbacks?

    a. 2
    b. 3
    c. 4
    d. 5

7. Troy Glaus was named to four All-Star Games over the course of his 13-season MLB career.

    a. True
    b. False

8. How many Gold Glove Awards did Orlando Hudson win over the course of his 11-season MLB career?

    a. 1
    b. 2

c. 3

d. 4

9. How many seasons did Stephen Drew spend with the Arizona Diamondbacks?

    a. 6

    b. 7

    c. 9

    d. 11

10. Over the course of his 13-season MLB career, Mark Reynolds played for the Arizona Diamondbacks, Colorado Rockies, St. Louis Cardinals, Cleveland Indians, Washington Nationals, New York Yankees, Milwaukee Brewers, and which team?

    a. Texas Rangers

    b. Boston Red Sox

    c. San Diego Padres

    d. Baltimore Orioles

11. How many All-Star Games was Jeff Cirillo named to over the course of his 14-season MLB career?

    a. 1

    b. 2

    c. 3

    d. 4

12. Tony Clark spent 5 seasons of his MLB career with the Arizona Diamondbacks.

    a. True

    b. False

13. How many All-Star Games was David Eckstein named to over the course of his 10-season MLB career?

    a. 1
    b. 2
    c. 3
    d. 4

14. Over the course of his 14-season MLB career, Willie Bloomquist played for the Arizona Diamondbacks, Kansas City Royals, Cincinnati Reds, and which other franchise?

    a. Seattle Mariners
    b. Oakland A's
    c. Los Angeles Dodgers
    d. Philadelphia Phillies

15. How many Silver Slugger Awards did Aaron Hill win over the course of his 13-season MLB career?

    a. 0
    b. 1
    c. 2
    d. 3

16. Eric Chavez won six Gold Glove Awards over the course of his 17-season MLB career.

    a. True
    b. False

17. Didi Gregorius has played for the Arizona Diamondbacks, Philadelphia Phillies, Cincinnati Reds, and which team?

a. Houston Astros

b. Seattle Mariners

c. New York Yankees

d. Minnesota Twins

18. How many seasons did Chris Owings spend with the Arizona Diamondbacks?

a. 2

b. 4

c. 6

d. 8

19. How many Gold Glove Awards has Nick Ahmed won?

a. 1

b. 2

c. 4

d. 5

20. Asdrubal Cabrera has been named to two All-Star Games.

a. True

b. False

QUIZ ANSWERS

1. B – 4

2. A – True

3. C – 5

4. D – 4

5. C – 6

6. D – 5

7. A – True

8. D – 4

9. B – 7

10. D – Baltimore Orioles

11. B – 2

12. A – True

13. B – 2

14. A – Seattle Mariners

15. C – 2

16. A – True

17. C – New York Yankees

18. C – 6

19. B – 2

20. A – True

DID YOU KNOW?

1. Paul Goldschmidt spent eight seasons of his MLB career with the Arizona Diamondbacks and currently plays for the St. Louis Cardinals. He is a six-time All-Star, three-time Gold Glove Award winner and four-time Silver Slugger Award winner.

2. Matt Williams spent six seasons of his 17-season MLB career with the Arizona Diamondbacks. He also played for the San Francisco Giants and Cleveland Indians. He is a five-time All-Star, 2001 World Series champion, four-time Gold Glove Award winner, four-time Silver Slugger Award winner, and the 2014 NL Manager of the Year Award winner.

3. Jay Bell spent five seasons of his 18-season MLB career with the Arizona Diamondbacks. He also played for the Pittsburgh Pirates, Cleveland Indians, New York Mets, and Kansas City Royals. He is a two-time All-Star, 2001 World Series champion, 1993 Gold Glove Award winner, and 1993 Silver Slugger Award winner.

4. Mark Grace spent three seasons of his 16-season MLB career with the Arizona Diamondbacks. He also played for the Chicago Cubs. He is a three-time All-Star, four-time Gold Glove Award winner, and a 2001 World Series champion.

5. Craig Counsell spent six of his 16-season MLB career with the Arizona Diamondbacks. He also played for the Milwaukee Brewers, Florida Marlins, Colorado Rockies, and Los Angeles Dodgers. He is a two-time World Series champion and 2001 NLCS MVP. Counsell is currently manager of the Milwaukee Brewers.

6. Orlando Hudson spent three of his 11-season MLB career with the Arizona Diamondbacks. He also played for the Toronto Blue Jays, San Diego Padres, Minnesota Twins, Los Angeles Dodgers, and Chicago White Sox. He is a two-time All-Star and four-time Gold Glove Award winner.

7. Tony Clark spent five of his 15-season MLB career with the Arizona Diamondbacks. He also played for the Detroit Tigers, New York Mets, San Diego Padres, New York Yankees, and Boston Red Sox. He is a 2001 All-Star.

8. Aaron Hill spent five of his 13-season MLB career with the Arizona Diamondbacks. He also played for the Toronto Blue Jays, San Francisco Giants, Boston Red Sox, and Milwaukee Brewers. He is a 2009 All-Star and two-time Silver Slugger Award winner.

9. Eric Chavez spent two of his 17-season MLB career with the Arizona Diamondbacks. He also played for the Oakland A's and New York Yankees. He is a six-time Gold Glove Award winner and 2002 Silver Slugger Award winner.

10. Nick Ahmed has been with the Arizona Diamondbacks since 2014. He has spent his entire career with the Dbacks, so far. He is a two-time Gold Glove Award winner.

CHAPTER 12:

PITCHERS AND CATCHERS

QUIZ TIME!

1. What year was Randy Johnson inducted into the National Baseball Hall of Fame?

    a. 2013
    b. 2014
    c. 2015
    d. 2016

2. Brandon Webb spent his entire seven-season MLB career with the Arizona Diamondbacks.

    a. True
    b. False

3. How many All-Star Games was Curt Schilling named to over the course of his 20-season MLB career?

    a. 2
    b. 4
    c. 6
    d. 8

4. How many seasons did Miguel Montero spend with the Arizona Diamondbacks?

    a. 6

    b. 7

    c. 8

    d. 9

5. How many Cy Young Awards has Zack Greinke won?

    a. 0

    b. 1

    c. 2

    d. 3

6. How many All-Star Games was Dan Haren named to over the course of his 13-season MLB career?

    a. 0

    b. 1

    c. 2

    d. 3

7. Stephen Vogt has been named to two All-Star Games.

    a. True

    b. False

8. How many All-Star Games was Dan Plesac named to over the course of his 18-season MLB career?

    a. 1

    b. 2

    c. 3

    d. 4

9. Over the course of his 12-season MLB career, Armando Reynoso played for the Arizona Diamondbacks, New York Mets, Atlanta Braves and which other franchise?

   a. Montreal Expos
   b. Colorado Rockies
   c. Texas Rangers
   d. Houston Astros

10. How many seasons did Damian Miller spend with the Arizona Diamondbacks?

   a. 3
   b. 4
   c. 5
   d. 6

11. How many Cy Young Awards has Max Scherzer won?

   a. 1
   b. 2
   c. 3
   d. 4

12. Gregg Olson was named the 1989 American League Rookie of the Year.

   a. True
   b. False

13. How many different MLB teams did Edwin Jackson play for over the course of his 17-season MLB career?

   a. 4
   b. 7

c. 10

d. 14

14. How many seasons did Brad Ziegler spend with the Arizona Diamondbacks?

    a. 9

    b. 8

    c. 7

    d. 6

15. How many All-Star Games has Patrick Corbin been named to?

    a. 1

    b. 2

    c. 3

    d. 4

16. Wade Miley was named the 2012 National League Rookie of the Year.

    a. True

    b. False

17. How many seasons did J.J. Putz spend with the Arizona Diamondbacks?

    a. 4

    b. 5

    c. 6

    d. 7

18. How many Silver Slugger Awards has Madison Bumgarner won?

    a. 1

    b. 2

    c. 3

    d. 4

19. Trevor Bauer has played for the Arizona Diamondbacks, Cincinnati Reds, Los Angeles Dodgers, and which team?

    a. Chicago Cubs

    b. New York Yankees

    c. Oakland A's

    d. Cleveland Indians

20. Trevor Cahill spent three seasons of his MLB career with the Arizona Diamondbacks.

    a. True

    b. False

QUIZ ANSWERS

1. C – 2015

2. A – True

3. C – 6

4. D – 9

5. B – 1

6. D – 3

7. A – True

8. C – 3

9. B – Colorado Rockies

10. C – 5

11. C – 3

12. A – True

13. D – 14

14. C – 7

15. B – 2

16. B – False (He came in 2nd place)

17. A – 4

18. B – 2

19. D – Cleveland Indians

20. A – True

DID YOU KNOW?

1. Randy Johnson spent eight seasons of his 22-season MLB career with the Arizona Diamondbacks. He also played for the Seattle Mariners, Montreal Expos, New York Yankees, San Francisco Giants, and Houston Astros. He is a member of the National Baseball Hall of Fame, five-time Cy Young Award winner, 10-time All-Star, 2001 World Series champion, 2001 World Series MVP, and led the league in ERA four times.

2. Brandon Webb spent his entire seven-season MLB career with the Arizona Diamondbacks. He is a three-time All-Star and 2006 NL Cy Young Award winner.

3. Curt Schilling spent four of his 20-season MLB career with the Arizona Diamondbacks. He also played for the Boston Red Sox, Philadelphia Phillies, Baltimore Orioles, and Houston Astros. He is a six-time All-Star, three-time World Series champion, 2001 World Series MVP, and 1993 NLCS MVP.

4. Miguel Montero spent nine of his 13-season MLB career with the Arizona Diamondbacks. He also played for the Chicago Cubs, Washington Nationals, and Toronto Blue Jays. He is a two-time All-Star and 2016 World Series champion.

5. Zack Greinke spent four seasons of his MLB career with the Arizona Diamondbacks and currently plays for the

Houston Astros. He has also played for the Kansas City Royals, Los Angeles Dodgers, Milwaukee Brewers, and Los Angeles Angels. He won the 2009 AL Cy Young Award, he is a six-time All-Star, six-time Gold Glove Award winner, two-time Silver Slugger Award winner, and led the league in ERA twice.

6. Max Scherzer spent two seasons of his MLB career with the Arizona Diamondbacks. He currently plays for the Washington Nationals. He has also played for the Detroit Tigers. He is a three-time Cy Young Award winner, seven-time All-Star, and 2019 World Series champion.

7. Patrick Corbin spent 6 seasons of his MLB career with the Arizona Diamondbacks. He currently plays for the Washington Nationals. He is a two-time All-Star and 2019 World Series champion.

8. Madison Bumgarner currently plays for the Arizona Diamondbacks. He also spent 11 seasons with the San Francisco Giants. He is a four-time All-Star, three-time World Series Champion, two-time Silver Slugger Award winner, 2014 World Series MVP, and 2014 NLCS MVP.

9. Trevor Bauer spent one season of his MLB career with the Arizona Diamondbacks and currently plays for the Los Angeles Dodgers. He has also played for the Cleveland Indians and Cincinnati Reds. He won the 2020 NL Cy Young Award, was a 2018 All-Star, and led the league in ERA in 2020.

10. J.J. Putz spent four seasons of his MLB career with the Arizona Diamondbacks. He also played for the Seattle Mariners, New York Mets, and Chicago White Sox. He is a 2007 All-Star and 2007 AL Rolaids Relief Man of the Year Award winner.

CHAPTER 13:

WORLD SERIES

QUIZ TIME!

1. How many World Series championships have the Arizona Diamondbacks won in franchise history?

    a. 0
    b. 1
    c. 2
    d. 3

2. How many NL Pennants have the Arizona Diamondbacks won

    a. 1
    b. 2
    c. 3
    d. 4

3. How many Wild Card berths have the Arizona Diamondbacks won?

    a. 0
    b. 1

c. 2

d. 3

4. Which team did the Arizona Diamondbacks face in the 2001 World Series?

    a. Anaheim Angels

    b. Seattle Mariners

    c. Oakland A's

    d. New York Yankees

5. How many games did the 2001 World Series go?

    a. 4

    b. 5

    c. 6

    d. 7

6. Who was the manager of the Arizona Diamondbacks during the 2001 World Series?

    a. Buck Showalter

    b. Al Pedrique

    c. Bob Brenly

    d. Bob Melvin

7. The 2001 World Series took place from October 27-November 4.

    a. True

    b. False

8. Who was the manager of the New York Yankees during the 2001 World Series?

a. Buck Showalter

b. Joe Torre

c. Joe Girardi

d. Lou Piniella

9. What was the final score of Game 1 of the 2001 World Series?

a. Dbacks 3, Yankees 2

b. Dbacks 2, Yankees 3

c. Dbacks 9, Yankees 1

d. Dbacks 1, Yankees 9

10. What was the final score of Game 2 of the 2001 World Series?

a. Dbacks 0, Yankees 4

b. Dbacks 4, Yankees 0

c. Dbacks 7, Yankees 4

d. Dbacks 4, Yankees 7

11. What was the final score of Game 3 of the 2001 World Series?

a. Dbacks 6, Yankees 12

b. Dbacks 12, Yankees 6

c. Dbacks 1, Yankees 2

d. Dbacks 2, Yankees 1

12. The Yankees won Game 4 of the 2001 World Series 4-3.

a. True

b. False

13. What was the final score of Game 5 of the 2001 World Series?

    a. Dbacks 2, Yankees 3
    b. Dbacks 3, Yankees 2
    c. Dbacks 7, Yankees 4
    d. Dbacks 4, Yankees 7

14. What was the final score of Game 6 of the 2001 World Series?

    a. Dbacks 2, Yankees 5
    b. Dbacks 5, Yankees 2
    c. Dbacks 2, Yankees 15
    d. Dbacks 15, Yankees 2

15. What was the final score of Game 7 of the 2001 World Series?

    a. Dbacks 2, Yankees 3
    b. Dbacks 3, Yankees 2
    c. Dbacks 10, Yankees 9
    d. Dbacks 9, Yankees 10

16. The Arizona Diamondbacks won Game 7 of the 2001 World Series at home.

    a. True
    b. False

17. Who was the winning pitcher of Game 7 of the 2001 World Series?

    a. Brian Anderson
    b. Curt Schilling

c. Randy Johnson

d. Armando Reynoso

18. Which Arizona Diamondbacks player was named the 2001 World Series MVP?

    a. Randy Johnson
    b. Curt Schilling
    c. Luis Gonzalez
    d. Both A & B

19. Which Arizona Diamondbacks player hit a walk-off single to win Game 7 of the World Series?

    a. Matt Williams
    b. Luis Gonzalez
    c. Mark Grace
    d. Steve Finley

20. The 2001 World Series was the third World Series to end in a bases loaded walk-off hit.

    a. True
    b. False

QUIZ ANSWERS

1. B – 1

2. A – 1

3. B – 1

4. D – New York Yankees

5. D – 7

6. C – Bob Brenly

7. A – True

8. B – Joe Torre

9. C – Dbacks 9 – Yankees 1

10. B – Dbacks 4 – Yankees 0

11. C – Dbacks 1 – Yankees 2

12. A - True

13. A – Dbacks 2 – Yankees 3

14. D – Dbacks 15 – Yankees 2

15. B – Dbacks 3 – Yankees 2

16. A – True

17. C – Randy Johnson

18. D – Both A & B

19. B – Luis Gonzalez

20. A – True

DID YOU KNOW?

1. President George W. Bush threw out the ceremonial first pitch before Game 3 of the 2001 World Series at Yankee Stadium.

2. The 2001 World Series was the subject of the HBO documentary, *Nine Innings from Ground Zero.*

3. The start date of the 2001 World Series was pushed back due to the terrorist attacks on September 11th. The 2001 World Series was the first World Series to extend into the month of November.

4. The 2001 World Series remains the last World Series to end with a walk-off.

5. The home team won every game in the 2001 World Series.

6. Game 7 of the 2001 World Series was named the "Best Postseason Game of the Decade" in 2009 by Sports Illustrated.

7. The attendance at Bank One Ballpark for Game 7 of the 2001 World Series was 49,589.

8. In 2001, the Arizona Diamondbacks beat the St. Louis Cardinals in five games in the NLDS. They beat the Atlanta Braves in five games in the NLCS.

9. The 2001 World Series was the first World Series to be played in the state of Arizona and the first to be played in the Mountain Time Zone.

10. The 2001 Arizona Diamondbacks were the first sports team from the state of Arizona to win a championship. The Dbacks were also the quickest MLB team to ever win a World Series (they had only been around for four years at that point).

CHAPTER 14:

HEATED RIVALRIES

QUIZ TIME!

1. Which team does NOT play in the National League West with the Arizona Diamondbacks?

    a. Los Angeles Dodgers

    b. Colorado Rockies

    c. Houston Astros

    d. San Diego Padres

2. The Atlanta Braves were a part of the National League West Division from 1969-1993.

    a. True

    b. False

3. Which team below was a member of the NL West Division from 1969-1993?

    a. Florida Marlins

    b. Milwaukee Brewers

    c. Cincinnati Reds

    d. Chicago Cubs

4. What current National League West team has the most NL West championships?

    a. San Francisco Giants
    b. Los Angeles Dodgers
    c. San Diego Padres
    d. Arizona Diamondbacks

5. The Houston Astros were members of the National League West from 1969-1993.

    a. True
    b. False

6. Which team won the National League West in 2020?

    a. Colorado Rockies
    b. Arizona Diamondbacks
    c. San Diego Padres
    d. Los Angeles Dodgers

7. The Colorado Rockies have never won a NL West Division Championship.

    a. True
    b. False

8. The Arizona Diamondbacks have won one World Series championship. How many do the Los Angeles Dodgers have?

    a. 5
    b. 7
    c. 9
    d. 12

9. The Arizona Diamondbacks have won one World Series championship. How many do the San Diego Padres have?

   a. 0
   b. 1
   c. 2
   d. 3

10. The Arizona Diamondbacks have won one World Series championship. How many do the San Francisco Giants have?

    a. 2
    b. 4
    c. 6
    d. 8

11. The Arizona Diamondbacks have won one World Series championship. How many do the Colorado Rockies have?

    a. 0
    b. 1
    c. 2
    d. 3

12. The Arizona Diamondbacks were members of the American League West division from 1998-2000.

    a. True
    b. False

13. Which player has NOT played for both the Arizona Diamondbacks and the Colorado Rockies?

a. Eric Byrnes

b. Randy Johnson

c. Steve Finley

d. Mark Reynolds

14. Which player has NOT played for both the Arizona Diamondbacks and the San Francisco Giants?

a. Madison Bumgarner

b. Cody Ross

c. Zack Greinke

d. Matt Williams

15. Which player has NOT played for both the Arizona Diamondbacks and the San Diego Padres?

a. Roberto Alomar

b. Justin Upton

c. Trevor Cahill

d. Luis Gonzalez

16. The National League West division was formed in 1969.

a. True

b. False

17. Which player has NOT played for both the Arizona Diamondbacks and the Los Angeles Dodgers?

a. Justin Upton

b. Trevor Bauer

c. A.J. Pollock

d. Steve Finley

18. How many National League West division titles did the Cincinnati Reds win before they moved to the NL Central?

    a. 0
    b. 2
    c. 5
    d. 7

19. How many National League West division titles did the Atlanta Braves win before they moved to the NL East?

    a. 0
    b. 1
    c. 3
    d. 5

20. The Houston Astros won two National League West division championships before they moved to the NL Central.

    a. True
    b. False

QUIZ ANSWERS

1. C – Houston Astros

2. A – True

3. C – Cincinnati Reds

4. B – Los Angeles Dodgers (19)

5. A – True

6. D – Los Angeles Dodgers

7. A – True

8. B – 7

9. A – 0

10. D – 8

11. A – 0

12. B – False

13. B – Randy Johnson

14. C – Zack Greinke

15. D – Luis Gonzalez

16. A – True

17. A – Justin Upton

18. D – 7

19. D – 5

20. A – True

DID YOU KNOW?

1. The Los Angeles Dodgers have the most National League West division championships with 19. The San Francisco Giants have eight, the San Diego Padres have five, the Arizona Diamondbacks have five and the Colorado Rockies have zero. The Cincinnati Reds won seven division championships during their time in the NL West. The Atlanta Braves won five division championships during their time in the NL West. The Houston Astros won two division championships during their time in the NL West. The most recent NL West Division champions were the Los Angeles Dodgers when they also won the 2020 World Series.

2. The Atlanta Braves were the first National League West division champions in 1969.

3. The Los Angeles Dodgers, San Diego Padres and San Francisco Giants are all founding members of the National League West. The Rockies joined as an expansion team in 1993 and the Arizona Diamondbacks joined as an expansion team in 1998.

4. The Los Angeles Dodgers have earned two Wild Card berths, the San Francisco Giants have earned three, the Arizona Diamondbacks and San Diego Padres each have one. The Colorado Rockies have the most Wild Card berths in the NL West with five so far in franchise history.

5. The Colorado Rockies and San Diego Padres are the only teams in the National League West who have NOT yet won a World Series championship.

6. The last time the Arizona Diamondbacks won the NL West was in 2011.

7. Henry Blanco, Eric Byrnes, Jhoulys Chacin, Jeff Cirillo, Greg Colbrunn, Craig Counsell, Jack Cust, Daniel Descalso, Alan Embree, Steve Finley, Greg Holland, Chris Ianetta, Joe Kennedy, Quinton McCracken, Melvin Mora, Chris Owings, Jordan Pacheco, Gerardo Parra, Armando Reynoso, Mark Reynolds, Jorge De La Rosa, and Tony Womack have all played for both the Arizona Diamondbacks and the Colorado Rockies.

8. Madison Bumgarner, Trevor Cahill, Alan Embree, Steve Finley, Aaron Hill, Randy Johnson, Terry Mulholland, Xavier Nady, Gerardo Parra, Cody Ross, Reggie Sanders, Stephen Vogt, and Matt Williams have all played for both the Arizona Diamondbacks and the San Francisco Giants.

9. Roberto Alomar, Heath Bell, Henry Blanco, Craig Breslow, Trevor Cahill, Jhoulys Chacin, Jeff Cirillo, Tony Clark, Jack Cust, David Eckstein, Alan Embree, Steve Finley, Scott Hairston, Orlando Hudson, Edwin Jackson, Jon Jay, Ian Kennedy, Xavier Nady, Micah Owings, Carlos Quentin, Adam Rosales, Reggie Sanders and Justin Upton have all played for both the Arizona Diamondbacks and the San Diego Padres.

10. Rod Barajas, Trevor Bauer, Henry Blanco, Albert Callaspo, Chris Capuano, Randy Choate, Craig Counsell, Steve Finley, Luis Gonzalez, Shawn Green, Zack Greinke, Dan Haren, Orlando Hudson, Edwin Jackson, Brandon McCarthy, Terry Mulholland, Gregg Olson, A.J. Pollock, Josh Reddick, Cody Ross, and Steve Souza Jr. have all played for both the Arizona Diamondbacks and the Los Angeles Dodgers.

CHAPTER 15:

THE AWARDS SECTION

QUIZ TIME!

1. Who is the only Arizona Diamondbacks player to win a Hank Aaron Award so far in franchise history?

   a. A.J. Pollock
   b. Ketel Marte
   c. Paul Goldschmidt
   d. Steve Finley

2. Steve Finley won Gold Glove Awards with the Arizona Diamondbacks in 1999 and 2000.

   a. True
   b. False

3. Who is the only Arizona Diamondbacks player to win a Roberto Clemente Award so far in franchise history?

   a. Justin Upton
   b. Randy Johnson
   c. Brandon Webb
   d. Curt Schilling

4. Which Arizona Diamondbacks player won a Gold Glove Award in 2019?

    a. Nick Ahmed
    b. Zack Greinke
    c. David Peralta
    d. All of the Above

5. Which Arizona Diamondbacks player won a Silver Slugger Award in 2012?

    a. Paul Goldschmidt
    b. Aaron Hill
    c. Willie Bloomquist
    d. Justin Upton

6. Which Arizona Diamondbacks manager won the NL Manager of the Year Award in 2007?

    a. Bob Brenly
    b. A.J. Hinch
    c. Kirk Gibson
    d. Bob Melvin

7. No Arizona Diamondbacks player has ever won the MLB Home Run Derby.

    a. True
    b. False

8. Which Arizona Diamondbacks player was named the DHL Hometown Hero, voted by MLB fans as the most outstanding player in franchise history?

a. Randy Johnson

b. Luis Gonzalez

c. Matt Williams

d. Jay Bell

9. Who was the first Arizona Diamondbacks player to win a Gold Glove Award?

a. Orlando Hudson

b. Gerardo Parra

c. Steve Finley

d. Luis Gonzalez

10. Who was the first Arizona Diamondbacks player to win a Silver Slugger Award?

a. Micah Owings

b. Luis Gonzalez

c. Daniel Hudson

d. Justin Upton

11. How many Cy Young Awards did Randy Johnson win during his time with the Arizona Diamondbacks?

a. 1

b. 2

c. 3

d. 4

12. Brandon Webb won a Cy Young Award in 2006.

a. True

b. False

13. Which Arizona Diamondbacks manager won the 2011 NL Manager of the Year Award?

   a. Chip Hale
   b. Bob Melvin
   c. Kirk Gibson
   d. A.J. Hinch

14. In 2007, who won the NL Rolaids Relief Man Award?

   a. Juan Cruz
   b. Brandon Lyon
   c. Tony Pena
   d. Jose Valverde

15. How many Luis Gonzalez Awards did Paul Goldschmidt win during his time with the Arizona Diamondbacks?

   a. 1
   b. 2
   c. 3
   d. 4

16. No Arizona Diamondbacks player has ever won a NL Rookie of the Year Award.

   a. True
   b. False

17. Which Arizona Diamondbacks player won a Silver Slugger Award in 2018?

   a. Aaron Hill
   b. Paul Goldschmidt

c. David Peralta

d. Both B & C

18. How many Gold Glove Awards did Paul Goldschmidt win during his time with the Arizona Diamondbacks?

a. 1

b. 2

c. 3

d. 4

19. How many Silver Slugger Awards did Paul Goldschmidt win during his time with the Arizona Diamondbacks?

a. 1

b. 2

c. 3

d. 4

20. Torey Lovullo was named the 2017 NL Manager of the Year.

a. True

b. False

QUIZ ANSWERS

1. C – Paul Goldschmidt (2013)

2. A – True

3. D – Curt Schilling

4. D – All of the Above

5. B – Aaron Hill

6. D – Bob Melvin

7. B – False (Luis Gonzalez – 2001)

8. A – Randy Johnson

9. C – Steve Finley (1999)

10. B – Luis Gonzalez (2001)

11. D – 4

12. A – True

13. C – Kirk Gibson

14. D – Jose Valverde

15. C – 3

16. A – True

17. D – Both B & C

18. C – 3

19. D – 4

20. A – True

DID YOU KNOW?

1. The Arizona Diamondbacks have had two different players win Cy Young Awards in franchise history Randy Johnson (1999, 2000, 2001, 2002) and Brandon Webb (2006).

2. The Arizona Diamondbacks have had eight different players win Silver Slugger Awards in franchise history Luis Gonzalez (2001), Micah Owings (2007), Justin Upton (2011), Daniel Hudson (2011), Aaron Hill (2012), Paul Goldschmidt (2013, 2015, 2017, 2018), David Peralta (2018), and Zack Greinke (2019).

3. The Arizona Diamondbacks have had three managers named National League Manager of the Year in franchise history Bob Melvin (2007), Kirk Gibson (2011), and Torey Lovullo (2017).

4. The Arizona Diamondbacks have had 8 different players win Gold Glove Awards in franchise history Steve Finley (1999, 2000, 2004), Orlando Hudson (2006, 2007), Gerardo Parra (2011, 2013), Paul Goldschmidt (2013, 2015, 2017), A.J. Pollock (2015), Zack Greinke (2016-2019), Nick Ahmed (2018, 2019) and David Peralta (2019).

5. No Arizona Diamondbacks player has won a National League MVP Award so far in franchise history.

6. The Luis Gonzalez Award is given annually to the Arizona Diamondbacks player who best exemplifies

Gonzalez's spirit both on and off the field. So far in franchise history, three different players have won the award Paul Goldschmidt (2015, 2017, 2018), Chris Owings (2016), and Eduardo Escobar (2019, 2020).

7. No Arizona Diamondbacks player has won a National League Comeback Player of the Year Award so far in franchise history.

8. No Arizona Diamondbacks player has won a Platinum Glove Award so far in franchise history.

9. Steve Finley finished his career with five Gold Glove Awards.

10. Randy Johnson finished his career with five Cy Young Awards.

CHAPTER 16:

THE VALLEY OF THE SUN

QUIZ TIME!

1. Where does Phoenix rank within the largest cities in the United States?

    a. 3rd

    b. 6th

    c. 11th

    d. 15th

2. Phoenix's elevation is more than 1,000 feet.

    a. True

    b. False

3. How many golf courses does the Greater Phoenix Area have?

    a. Over 50

    b. Over 100

    c. Over 150

    d. Over 200

4. MLB Spring Training takes place in Arizona and Florida. The Grapefruit League consists of the teams that host spring training in Florida. What is the name of the league in Arizona?

    a. Sun League
    b. Valley League
    c. Cactus League
    d. Desert League

5. What is the name of the PGA Tour stop in Phoenix that draws in more spectators than any other PGA event?

    a. Safeway Open
    b. Waste Management Open
    c. Farmers Insurance Open
    d. Honda Classic

6. The Hotel San Carlos in downtown Phoenix is featured in the opening scene of which horror movie?

    a. *The Texas Chainsaw Massacre*
    b. *Scream*
    c. *The Shining*
    d. *Psycho*

7. Phoenix has the most sunny days of any metro U.S. city.

    a. True
    b. False

8. What is the name of Phoenix's NFL team?

    a. Arizona Broncos
    b. Arizona Dolphins

c. Arizona Cardinals

d. Arizona Jaguars

9. What is the name of Phoenix's NBA team?

a. Phoenix Magic

b. Phoenix Suns

c. Phoenix Warriors

d. Phoenix Pelicans

10. What is the name of Phoenix's NHL team?

a. Arizona Lightning

b. Arizona Wild

c. Arizona Sharks

d. Arizona Coyotes

11. Where do the Arizona Cardinals play?

a. CenturyLink Field

b. State Farm Stadium

c. Nissan Stadium

d. U.S. Bank Stadium

12. Arizona does not participate in Daylight Savings Time.

a. True

b. False

13. Where do the Phoenix Suns play?

a. American Airlines Center

b. Chase Center

c. Talking Stick Resort Arena

d. Smoothie King Center

14. The saguaro cactus, found in Phoenix, cannot be found in any other desert in the world.

    a. True
    b. False

15. Where do the Arizona Coyotes play?

    a. Little Caesars Arena
    b. SAP Center
    c. T-Mobile Arena
    d. Gila River Arena

16. Phoenix is the only state capital with a population over 1 million residents.

    a. True
    b. False

17. The Phoenix Zoo is the largest privately-owned, non-profit zoo in the United States.

    a. True
    b. False

18. What is Sky Harbor International Airport's code?

    a. SHI
    b. SHA
    c. PHX
    d. PIX

19. How many times has Phoenix hosted the Super Bowl?

    a. 0
    b. 1

c. 2

d. 3

20. Arizona is the only U.S. state to have a part of all four North American deserts within their state.

    a. True

    b. False

QUIZ ANSWERS

1. B – 6th

2. A - True

3. D – Over 200

4. C – Cactus League

5. B – Waste Management Open

6. D – *Psycho*

7. A – True

8. C – Arizona Cardinals

9. B – Phoenix Suns

10. D – Arizona Coyotes

11. B – State Farm Stadium

12. A – True

13. C – Talking Stick Resort Arena

14. A – True

15. D – Gila River Arena

16. A – True

17. A – True

18. C – PHX

19. D – 3

20. A – True

DID YOU KNOW?

1. Arizona is home to over 22 Native American tribes and/or nations, which is the most of any U.S. state.

2. Two NASCAR events are held each racing season at the Phoenix International Raceway.

3. The Desert Botanical Garden in Phoenix is home to one of the largest collections of desert plants in the world.

4. Phoenix is home to the headquarters of five Fortune 500 companies Avnet, Freeport-McMoRan, Republic Services, Insight Enterprises, and Magellan Health.

5. The Arizona Biltmore Hotel's Catalina Pool was Marilyn Monroe's favorite pool.

6. it can take a saguaro cactus between 50-100 years to grow its "arms." Cutting down a saguaro in Arizona is a class four felony, even if it is on your own property.

7. On average, it is 100 degrees or hotter for over 100 days each year in Phoenix.

8. The BMO Tower in Midtown Phoenix was built for the Dial Corporation in 1991. It was built to be shaped like a bar of Dial soap.

9. The South Mountain Park and Preserve is one of the largest municipal parks in North America. It contains 50 miles of hiking/biking trails.

10. Phoenix is home to college football's Fiesta Bowl and Guaranteed Rate Bowl.

CHAPTER 17:

SCHILL

QUIZ TIME!

1. Over the course of his 20-season MLB career, Curt Schilling played for the Arizona Diamondbacks, Boston Red Sox, Baltimore Orioles, Houston Astros and which team?

    a. Los Angeles Dodgers
    b. Philadelphia Phillies
    c. St. Louis Cardinals
    d. New York Yankees

2. Curt Schilling was born on November 14, 1966.

    a. True
    b. False

3. Where was Curt Schilling born?

    a. Prescott, Arizona
    b. Phoenix, Arizona
    c. Anchorage, Alaska
    d. Juneau, Alaska

4. How many All-Star Games was Curt Schilling named to over the course of his 20-season MLB career?

    a. 2
    b. 4
    c. 6
    d. 8

5. Curt Schilling's full name is Curtis Montague Schilling.

    a. True
    b. False

6. How many World Series championships did Curt Schilling win over the course of his 20-season MLB career?

    a. 1
    b. 2
    c. 3
    d. 4

7. How many times did Curt Schilling lead the MLB in wins over the course of his 20-season MLB career?

    a. 1
    b. 2
    c. 3
    d. 4

8. Curt Schilling was named the 1993 NLCS MVP.

    a. True
    b. False

9. During the 2004 World Series with the Boston Red Sox, Schilling pitched with blood on which garment?

    a. Hat
    b. Pantleg
    c. Shirt
    d. Sock

10. How many times did Curt Schilling lead the National League in strikeouts over the course of his 20-season MLB career?

    a. 1
    b. 2
    c. 3
    d. 4

11. Curt Schilling won a Roberto Clemente Award in which year?

    a. 1998
    b. 1999
    c. 2000
    d. 2001

12. Curt Schilling did NOT win a Gold Glove Award over the course of his 20-season MLB career.

    a. True
    b. False

13. How many Cy Young Awards did Curt Schilling win over the course of his 20-season MLB career?

a. 0

b. 1

c. 2

d. 3

14. Curt Schilling is a member of the Boston Red Sox Hall of Fame and the Philadelphia Phillies Wall of Fame.

a. True

b. False

15. How many 300 strikeout seasons did Curt Schilling have over the course of his 20-season MLB career?

a. 1

b. 2

c. 3

d. 4

16. How many times did Curt Schilling lead the National League in complete games over the course of his 20-season MLB career?

a. 1

b. 2

c. 3

d. 4

17. Curt Schilling won a Branch Rickey Award in 2001.

a. True

b. False

18. What is Curt Schilling's career ERA?

a. 2.46

b. 2.76

c. 3.16

d. 3.46

19. How many total strikeouts did Curt Schilling collect over the course of his 20-season MLB career?

    a. 1, 116

    b. 2, 116

    c. 3, 116

    d. 4, 116

20. Curt Schilling was named a 2001 World Series MVP along with teammate, Randy Johnson.

    a. True

    b. False

QUIZ ANSWERS

1. B – Philadelphia Phillies

2. A – True

3. C – Anchorage, Alaska

4. C – 6

5. A – True

6. C – 3

7. B – 2 (2001, 2004)

8. A – True

9. D – Sock

10. B – 2 (1997, 1998)

11. D – 2001

12. A – True

13. A – 0

14. A – True

15. C – 3 (1996, 1997, 2002)

16. D – 4 (1996, 1998, 2000, 2001)

17. A – True

18. D – 3.46

19. C – 3, 116

20. A – True

DID YOU KNOW?

1. Curt Schilling's career win-loss record is 216-146.

2. Curt Schilling pitched 3,261 innings over the course of his MLB career.

3. Curt Schilling is a two-time Baseball Digest Pitcher of the Year Award winner (2001, 2004).

4. Curt Schilling is a four-time MLB Pitcher of the Month Award winner. He is a three-time MLB Player of the Week Award winner.

5. Curt Schilling is a two-time Sporting News NL Pitcher of the Year Award winner (2001, 2002). He was also named their Sportsman of the Year in 2001.

6. Curt Schilling is a two-time Sports Illustrated Sportsperson of the Year (2001, 2004).

7. In 2014, Curt Schilling was diagnosed with mouth cancer. He used his experience to warn future Dbacks pitcher Madison Bumgarner about the dangers of chewing tobacco.

8. Curt Schilling's son, Gehrig was named after baseball legend Lou Gehrig who suffered from ALS. Schilling has an ALS charity called "Curt's Pitch for ALS."

9. In 2013, Curt Schilling's bloody sock from the 2004 World Series was sold at auction for $92,613.

10. Curt Schilling has the highest strikeout-to-walk ratio of any member of the 3,000-strikeout club.

CHAPTER 18:

MATT THE BAT

QUIZ TIME!

1. What is Matt Williams' full name?

    a. Gerard Matthew Williams

    b. Matthew Gerard Williams

    c. Derrick Matthew Williams

    d. Matthew Derrick Williams

2. Matt Williams spent his entire 17-season MLB career with the Arizona Diamondbacks.

    a. True

    b. False

3. What MLB team was Matt Williams manager of from 2014-2015?

    a. San Francisco Giants

    b. Washington Nationals

    c. Cleveland Indians

    d. Oakland A's

4. How many All-Star Games was Matt Williams named to over the course of his 17-season MLB career?

    a. 1

    b. 3

    c. 5

    d. 7

5. How many World Series championships did Matt Williams win over the course of his 17-season MLB career?

    a. 1

    b. 2

    c. 3

    d. 5

6. How many Gold Glove Awards did Matt Williams win over the course of his 17-season MLB career?

    a. 2

    b. 4

    c. 6

    d. 8

7. Matt Williams appeared in the World Series with all three teams that he played for.

    a. True

    b. False

8. How many Silver Slugger Awards did Matt Williams win over the course of his 17-season MLB career?

    a. 1

    b. 2

c. 3

d. 4

9. What season did Matt Williams lead the NL in home runs?

    a. 1992

    b. 1993

    c. 1994

    d. 1995

10. What season did Matt Williams lead the NL in RBIs?

    a. 1990

    b. 1991

    c. 1993

    d. 1995

11. How many total home runs did Matt Williams hit over the course of his 17-season MLB career?

    a. 358

    b. 378

    c. 398

    d. 408

12. Matt Williams was named the 2014 National League Manager of the Year.

    a. True

    b. False

13. What is Matt Williams' career batting average?

    a. .228

    b. .268

c. .308

d. .328

14. How many total runs did Matt Williams score over the course of his 17-season MLB career?

   a. 777

   b. 887

   c. 997

   d. 1,007

15. How many total RBIs did Matt Williams collect over the course of his 17-season MLB career?

   a. 1,118

   b. 1,218

   c. 1,318

   d. 1,418

16. Matt Williams stole 53 bases in his MLB career.

   a. True

   b. False

17. Matt Williams was the third base coach for which team from 2017-2019?

   a. San Francisco Giants

   b. Cleveland Indians

   c. Oakland A's

   d. Tampa Bay Rays

18. How many total hits did Matt Williams collect over the course of his 17-season MLB career?

a. 1, 545

b. 1,676

c. 1,777

d. 1,878

19. How many total at-bats did Matt Williams have over the course of his 17-season MLB career?

   a. 4,000

   b. 5,000

   c. 6,000

   d. 7,000

20. Matt Williams was born on November 28, 1965, in Bishop, California.

   a. True

   b. False

QUIZ ANSWERS

1. D – Matthew Derrick Williams
2. B – False (Arizona Diamondbacks, San Francisco Giants and Cleveland Indians)
3. B – Washington Nationals
4. C – 5
5. A – 1 (2001)
6. B – 4
7. A – True
8. D – 4
9. C – 1994
10. A – 1990
11. B – 378
12. A – True
13. B - .268
14. C – 997
15. B – 1,218
16. A – True
17. C – Oakland A's
18. D – 1,878
19. D – 7,000
20. A – True

DID YOU KNOW?

1. Matt Williams is the grandson of former MLB outfielder Bert Griffith.

2. Matt Williams is the current manager of the KIA Tigers of the KBO League in South Korea.

3. Matt Williams coached for the Arizona Diamondbacks from 2010-2013 and in 2016.

4. Matt Williams attended the University of Nevada, Las Vegas.

5. Matt Williams made his MLB debut with the San Francisco Giants on April 11, 1987, against the Los Angeles Dodgers. Matt Williams played in his final MLB game with the Arizona Diamondbacks on May 31, 2003, against the San Diego Padres.

6. After getting a divorce from his first wife, Matt Williams requested a trade to the Arizona Diamondbacks to be closer to his children.

7. Matt Williams is a member of the San Francisco Giants Wall of Fame.

8. In 2017, Matt Williams became a studio analyst with NBC Sports Bay Area on San Francisco Giants pre- and post-game shows.

9. In 2007, Matt Williams was named in the Mitchell Report, accusing him of steroid use.

10. Matt Williams was named the MLB Player of the Month two times in his career. He was named the MLB Player of the Week four times in his career.

CHAPTER 19:

AMERICA'S PASTIME

QUIZ TIME!

1. How many total teams play in Major League Baseball?

    a. 15
    b. 20
    c. 30
    d. 33

2. Major League Baseball was founded in 1903.

    a. True
    b. False

3. Who is the current commissioner of Major League Baseball?

    a. Bart Giamatti
    b. Fay Vincent
    c. Bud Selig
    d. Rob Manfred

4. What year was the National League founded?

a. 1870

b. 1876

c. 1903

d. 1911

5. What year was the American League founded?

a. 1888

b. 1901

c. 1903

d. 1918

6. Major League Baseball is the second wealthiest professional sports league. Which league is the wealthiest?

a. NBA

b. NHL

c. NFL

d. MLS

7. The Major League Baseball headquarters is in New York City.

a. True

b. False

8. How many games does each Major League Baseball team play per season?

a. 92

b. 122

c. 162

d. 192

9. In which two U.S. states is Major League Baseball's spring training held?

    a. California and Florida
    b. Arizona and Florida
    c. Arizona and California
    d. California and Arizona

10. How many stitches does a Major League Baseball baseball have?

    a. 98
    b. 100
    c. 108
    d. 110

11. Where is the National Baseball Hall of Fame located?

    a. Denver, Colorado
    b. Phoenix, Arizona
    c. Los Angeles, California
    d. Cooperstown, New York

12. All 30 Major League Baseball teams are in the United States.

    a. True
    b. False

13. Which current Major League Baseball stadium is the oldest baseball stadium still in use?

    a. Angel Stadium
    b. Dodger Stadium

c. Fenway Park

d. Wrigley Field

14. Major League Baseball has the highest attendance of any sports league in the world.

   a. True

   b. False

15. Fill in the blank: Seventh Inning _____

   a. Jog

   b. Song

   c. Shake

   d. Stretch

16. William Howard Taft was the first United States president to throw out the ceremonial first pitch at a Major League Baseball game.

   a. True

   b. False

17. It is a Major League Baseball rule that all umpires must wear which color underwear in case they rip their pants?

   a. Tan

   b. Gray

   c. White

   d. Black

18. What year did the first Major League Baseball World Series take place?

   a. 1903

   b. 1905

c. 1915

d. 1920

19. Former Major League Baseball Commissioner Bart Giamatti is the father of actor Paul Giamatti.

    a. True

    b. False

20. The song traditionally played in the middle of the 7th inning at Major League Baseball games is called *Take Me Out to the Ballpark.*

    a. True

    b. False

QUIZ ANSWERS

1. C – 30

2. A – True

3. D – Rob Manfred

4. B – 1876

5. B – 1901

6. C – NFL

7. A – True

8. C – 162

9. B – Arizona and Florida

10. C – 108

11. D – Cooperstown, New York

12. B – False (The Toronto Blue Jays are located in Canada)

13. C – Fenway Park

14. A – True

15. D – Stretch

16. A – True

17. D – Black

18. A - 1903

19. A – True

20. B – False (*Take Me Out to the Ballgame*)

DID YOU KNOW?

1. The average lifespan of a baseball in a Major League Baseball game is seven pitches. This means approximately 5-6 dozen baseballs are used in every Major League Baseball game.

2. The Boston Americans won the very first Major League Baseball World Series. They defeated the Pittsburgh Pirates in eight games. Today the most games a World Series can go is seven.

3. The New York Yankees currently hold the most World Series titles in Major League Baseball with 27 total.

4. Hot dogs are the most popular food item sold at Major League Baseball ballparks. Over 21 million hot dogs were sold at MLB stadiums in 2014.

5. The longest Major League Baseball game on record occurred on May 9, 1984, between the Chicago White Sox and Milwaukee Brewers. The game lasted 8 hours, 6 minutes. The most innings played in a Major League Baseball game was the 26 innings on May 1, 1920, between the Brooklyn Dodgers and Boston Braves.

6. The mound to home plate distance at Major League Baseball ballparks is 60 feet, 6 inches.

7. Before they can be used in a Major League Baseball game, each MLB baseball is rubbed with a special mud to

improve grip and reduce luster. This special mud comes from a specific, secret location in the state of New Jersey.

8. The fastest Major League Baseball game on record took place on September 28, 1919. The game between the New York Giants and Philadelphia Phillies took 51 minutes. An average MLB game is 3 hours.

9. The American League uses a designated hitter. A DH only hits and does not play in the field. In the National League, the pitcher hits instead of using a designated hitter. If an interleague game is being played, whether a DH is used or not is determined by which team is the home team. If the home team is from the American League, each team will use a DH. If the home team is from the National League, each team's pitcher will hit.

10. The distance between each of the four bases in Major League Baseball is 90 feet.

CHAPTER 20:

GOATS

QUIZ TIME!

1. How many World Series championships did Babe Ruth win over the course of his 22-season career?

   a. 3
   b. 5
   c. 7
   d. 9

2. Jackie Robinson's uniform No. 42 was retired by all MLB teams in 1997.

   a. True
   b. False

3. How many All-Star Games was Willie Mays named to over the course of his 22-season MLB career?

   a. 8
   b. 14
   c. 20
   d. 24

4. How many National League batting titles did Tony Gwynn win over the course of his 20-season MLB career?

   a. 2

   b. 6

   c. 8

   d. 10

5. Rickey Henderson holds the all-time MLB record for most stolen bases. How many did Rickey steal over the course of his 25-season MLB career?

   a. 1,306

   b. 1,406

   c. 1,506

   d. 1,606

6. What year was Hank Aaron inducted into the National Baseball Hall of Fame?

   a. 1980

   b. 1981

   c. 1982

   d. 1983

7. Derek Jeter was named the 1996 American League Rookie of the Year.

   a. True

   b. False

8. How many Gold Glove Awards did Ken Griffey Jr. win over the course of his 22-season MLB career?

a. 7

b. 8

c. 9

d. 10

9. How many No-Hitters did Nolan Ryan throw over the course of his 27-season MLB career?

   a. 1

   b. 3

   c. 7

   d. 9

10. Ted Williams missed which season(s) due to military service?

    a. 1943

    b. 1944

    c. 1945

    d. All of the Above

11. How many times was Joe DiMaggio named MVP over the course of his 13-season career?

    a. 0

    b. 1

    c. 2

    d. 3

12. Stan Musial spent his entire 22-season MLB career with the St. Louis Cardinals.

    a. True

    b. False

13. What year was Reggie Jackson inducted into the National Baseball Hall of Fame?

    a. 1990
    b. 1993
    c. 1995
    d. 1999

14. Cal Ripken Jr. spent his entire 21-season MLB career with the Baltimore Orioles.

    a. True
    b. False

15. How many All-Star Games was Roberto Clemente named to over the course of his 18-season MLB career?

    a. 5
    b. 10
    c. 15
    d. 18

16. Johnny Bench spent his entire 17-season MLB career with the Cincinnati Reds.

    a. True
    b. False

17. How many times did Sandy Koufax lead the league in ERA over the course of his 12-season MLB career?

    a. 2
    b. 3
    c. 4
    d. 5

18. In which year was Frank Robinson named the National League Rookie of the Year?

    a. 1955

    b. 1956

    c. 1965

    d. 1966

19. Lou Gehrig spent his entire 17-season career with the New York Yankees.

    a. True

    b. False

20. Rod Carew was named the 1967 American League Rookie of the Year.

    a. True

    b. False

QUIZ ANSWERS

1. C – 7

2. A - True

3. D – 24

4. C – 8

5. B – 1,406

6. C – 1982

7. A – True

8. D – 10

9. C – 7

10. D – All of the Above

11. D – 3

12. A -True

13. B – 1993

14. A – True

15. C – 15

16. A – True

17. D – 5

18. B – 1956

19. A – True

20. A – True

DID YOU KNOW?

1. Babe Ruth spent his 22-season career with the New York Yankees, Boston Red Sox, and Boston Braves. He is a member of the National Baseball Hall of Fame, the 1923 American League MVP, two-time All-Star, seven-time World Series champion, won the 1924 batting title, and led the league in ERA in 1916. Ruth is often regarded as the greatest baseball player of all time.

2. Jackie Robinson spent his entire 10-season career with the Brooklyn Dodgers. He is a member of the National Baseball Hall of Fame, the 1949 National League MVP, six-time All-Star, 1955 World Series champion, the 1949 National league batting champion, and 1947 National League Rookie of the Year. Robinson is best known for breaking the color barrier in baseball.

3. Willie Mays spent his 22-season career with the San Francisco Giants and New York Mets. He is a member of the National Baseball Hall of Fame, two-time MVP, 1951 National League Rookie of the Year, 24-time All-Star, 1954 World Series Champion, 12-time Gold Glove Award winner, the 1954 National League batting champion, two-time All-Star Game MVP, and the 1954 Major League Player of the Year.

4. Tony Gwynn spent his entire 20-season career with the San Diego Padres. He is a member of the National

Baseball Hall of Fame, 15-time All-Star, five-time Gold Glove Award winner, seven-time Silver Slugger Award winner, and eight-time batting champion.

5. Rickey Henderson spent his 25-season career with the Oakland A's, New York Yankees, San Diego Padres, New York Mets, Boston Red Sox, Los Angeles Dodgers, Anaheim Angels, Seattle Mariners, and Toronto Blue Jays. He is a member of the National Baseball Hall of Fame, the 1990 American League MVP, two-time All-Star, two-time World Series champion. Henderson is often regarded as the greatest leadoff hitter of all time. He holds the MLB record for most stolen bases.

6. Hank Aaron spent his 23-season career with the Atlanta Braves and Milwaukee Brewers. He is a member of the National Baseball Hall of Fame, the 1957 National League MVP, 25-time All-Star, 1957 World Series champion, two-time NL batting champion and three-time Gold Glove Award winner.

7. Derek Jeter spent his entire 20-season career with the New York Yankees. He is a member of the National Baseball Hall of Fame, 14-time All-Star, 1996 American League Rookie of the Year, five-time World Series champion, the 2000 World Series MVP, the 2000 All-Star Game MVP, five-time Gold Glove Award winner and five-time Silver Slugger Award winner.

8. Stan Musial spent his entire 22-season career with the St. Louis Cardinals. He is a member of the National Baseball

Hall of Fame, three-time MVP, 24-time All-Star, three-time World Series champion, seven-time batting champion and two-time Major League Player of the Year.

9. Cal Ripken Jr. spent his entire 21-season career with the Baltimore Orioles. He is a member of the National Baseball Hall of Fame, two-time MVP, 19-time All-Star, 1982 American League Rookie of the Year, 1983 World Series champion, two-time Gold Glove Award winner, eight-time Silver Slugger Award winner, two-time All-Star Game MVP, and two-time Major League Player of the Year.

10. Sandy Koufax spent his entire 12-season career with the Los Angeles Dodgers. He is a member of the National Baseball Hall of Fame, the 1963 National League MVP, three-time Cy Young Award winner, three-time Triple Crown winner, seven-time All-Star, three-time World Series champion, two-time World Series MVP, led the National League in ERA five times, and two-time Major League Player of the Year.

CONCLUSION

Learn anything new? Now you truly are the ultimate Diamondbacks fan! Not only did you learn about the Dbacks of the modern era, but you also expanded your knowledge back to the early days of the franchise.

You learned about the Arizona Diamondbacks' origins and their history, plus about how far they've come. You learned about the history of their uniforms and jersey numbers and read some of the craziest nicknames of all time. You learned more about Big Unit, Randy Johnson. You also learned about Luis Gonzalez and Curt Schilling. Plus, who could forget about Matt Williams? You were amazed by Dbacks' stats and recalled some of the most infamous Dbacks trades, drafts, and draft picks of all time.

You broke down your knowledge by outfielders, infielders, pitchers, and catchers. You looked back on the Diamondbacks playoff feats and the awards that came before, after, and during them. You also learned about the Diamondbacks fiercest rivalries both within their division and out.

Every team in the MLB has a history, but the Arizona Diamondbacks have one of the most memorable of all. They have gone through winning seasons and losing seasons with the backing of their devoted fans. Being the ultimate Dbacks fan takes knowledge and a whole lot of patience, which you tested with this book. Whether you knew every answer or were stumped by several questions, you learned some of the most baffling history that the game of baseball has to offer.

The deep history of the Arizona Diamondbacks franchise represents what we all love about the game of baseball. The heart, the determination, the tough times, and the unexpected moments, plus the players that inspire us and encourage us to do our best because even if you get knocked down, there is always another game and another day.

With players like Ketel Marte, Nick Ahmed, and Eduardo Escobar, the future for the Arizona Diamondbacks continues to look bright. They have a lot to prove but there is no doubt that this franchise will continue to be one of the most competitive teams in Major League Baseball year after year. It's a new decade which means there is a clean slate, ready to continue writing the history of the Arizona Diamondbacks.

Made in the USA
Columbia, SC
13 May 2023

16634074R00098